JIM BECKWOURTH, *Crow Chief*
(1798–1867)

Books by OLIVE BURT

JIM BECKWOURTH: Crow Chief

BRIGHAM YOUNG

JOHN CHARLES FREMONT: Trail Marker of the Old West

OURAY THE ARROW

JEDEDIAH SMITH: Fur Trapper of the Old West

Jim
Beckwourth

CROW CHIEF

by Olive Burt

 JULIAN MESSNER, INC., NEW YORK

Published by JULIAN MESSNER, INC.
8 West 40 Street, New York 18

Published simultaneously in Canada
by The Copp Clark Publishing Co. Limited

MANUFACTURED IN THE UNITED STATES OF AMERICA
BY GEORGE MC KIBBIN & SON; BROOKLYN, NEW YORK

Library of Congress Catalog Card No. 57-11498

TO MABEL

Whose friendship through the years
has been unquestioning—unquestioned

Contents

xxxxxxxxxxxxxxxxxxxxxxxxxxxxxxxxxxxxxxxxxxxxxxxxxxxxxxxxx

1 INTRODUCTION TO VIOLENCE   9

2 JIM GROWS UP   20

3 THE GAUDY LIAR   33

4 AN ASHLEY MAN   42

5 OFF TO THE SHINING MOUNTAINS   54

6 JIM BECOMES A MOUNTAIN MAN   64

7 THE TRAPPER'S LIFE   77

8 A JOKE BACKFIRES   88

9 JIM MAKES GOOD   100

10 CHIEF OF THE CROWS   111

11 CIVILIZATION BECKONS   124

12 RESTLESS DAYS   137

13 JIM FOUNDS A CITY   146

14 THE TROUBLED WEST   157

15 AND AT THE END—A CROW   169

    BIBLIOGRAPHY   185

    INDEX   187

Contents

CHAPTER 1

Introduction to Violence

"You can be Mad Anthony if you want, but I'm going to be Major James Beckwourth!"

Nine-year-old Jim Beckwourth stood on a little hillock and stared defiantly at his twelve-year-old half brother Tom.

"You always want to be Pa!" Tom complained angrily. "And you can't. I'm going to be Pa this time!"

"You ain't! You ain't!" Jim shouted, his black eyes blazing, his fists clenched. "I'm really James Beckwourth. That's *my* name, and no one else is goin' to have it, even in play!"

Tom raised his fists. "We'll just see about that!" and he advanced toward the younger boy.

The other children stood back, their eyes round with excitement. Another fight between Jim and Tom! Nearly every game ended that way. But it didn't spoil the fun. It just made the pretend battle more real.

Jim didn't wait. He gave a leap from his slight elevation and lit astride Tom's crouching body. His fists began to pound his brother. Tom, older, larger, stronger, had all the advantage. He squirmed and dislodged Jim, tossed him to the ground and knelt over him, pummeling. The other children danced up and down, squealing.

There were some half-dozen boys and girls there in

the clearing in the Missouri woods that summer day of 1807. They were all between the ages of two and twelve, and were of various complexions from the deep black of four-year-old Susie to the light bronze shade of Jim and the ruddy, sandy complexion of Tom.

For this was the establishment of James Beckwourth, formerly a major in the American Revolution, where he had won some fame when he stormed Stony Point with General Mad Anthony Wayne. Major Beckwourth was a Virginian, and it was from Virginia that he joined the troops fighting against British domination. After the war, the major had returned to his native state, but two years ago he had picked up bag and baggage, family and servants, and had moved to the frontier.

There, near the confluence of the Missouri and Mississippi rivers, near the famous Portage des Sioux, the soldier had found what he had come looking for—a lovely piece of land, lush with grass, rich in timber, luxurious with water—and with two mighty rivers to afford transportation when he wished to travel. Here Major Beckwourth—for like others of the Revolutionary soldiers he clung to his military title throughout his life—had built a large log house for his wife and their son, Tom. Clustered near were the sturdy cabins for his twenty-two Negro servants and their children.

It was here, in the Negro cabins, that Jim lived, though he was the acknowledged son of his father and bore the Major's own name. The youngster had been born in Fredericksburg, Virginia on April 26, 1798, and was only seven years old when the move to Missouri was made.

On the fertile clearing Major Beckwourth had established a thriving farm, where he raised most of the essentials for living, together with cattle, pigs, chickens, and fine, blooded horses from the stock he had brought from his own beloved Virginia.

Everything on the place was thriving and prosperous and happy, excepting Young Jim. A tall, good-looking boy, he resembled his father far more than did his half brother Tom, who had his mother's fair skin and blue eyes. Jim's skin was a light, clear bronze, scarcely darker than his father's deeply tanned face. His hair was straight and black, with no hint of the kinkiness that appeared on so many of the little heads around him. His dark eyes, large and expressive, had an imperious cast, and his features were clear-cut, with a haughty aspect that was noticeable even when he was a baby. Perhaps his resemblance to his father had been marked from birth, for the major had given this child his own name.

The major had always shown a good deal of partiality for the intelligent, headstrong youngster. This was largely due to their similarity in taste and disposition and only partly to the fact that Jim's mother had died when he was born. The baby had thus been left largely to the care of his two half sisters, who had none of the major's blood in them.

When the family had first moved to Missouri, Jim, sensitive to the conditions around him, had been very happy. He had felt a relaxing of the formal life of the Virginia plantation. There, Tom's uncles and aunts and grandparents had somehow stood between Jim and his father. Here, on the frontier, the major treated Jim with the same affection and kindness that he showed to Tom. In the warmth of his father's love, Jim began to "feel his oats," as Tom's mother, Ma'am Beckwourth, sometimes said. He became arrogant, particularly toward Tom.

Jim loved his half sisters—Matilda, who, at the age of nine had taken his mother's place in his life, and Louise, a playmate and confidante. But Tom rubbed Jim the wrong way, bringing out latent resentment and hatred. Tom lived in the Big House, had a mother to caress him, would someday own the plantation and rule the slaves on it. Jim knew things had to be this way, but he felt sometimes that Tom was the usurper—that he, James Beckwourth, who bore his father's name and features, was the rightful heir.

On the other hand, Tom resented his father's partiality for the younger boy and hated Jim for his resemblance to the major. But he had learned that it did him no good to let his father know of his feeling. It was only when they were playing, and Jim became unbearable, that Tom let fly with his fists and with grim satisfaction pummeled the younger boy.

The two brothers were flailing each other now, each with desperate determination to make the other yell quits, when the unequal contest was brought to a sudden end.

"Tom!"

It was Major Beckwourth, and his voice told the boys what both well knew—their father did not permit fisticuffs among the children.

The major came toward the boys rolling on the ground. Taking hold of their shirts, one in each hand, he yanked them apart and set them on their feet.

"What is the meaning of this, Tom? Why do you pound a boy so much younger than yourself?"

"He started it!" Tom muttered resentfully.

Major Beckwourth's eyes rested on Young Jim and they softened as they took in the bitter mouth, the angry eyes, the haughty tilt to the unsubmissive head.

"Yes," he said, "yes, I suppose he did. Go to your

mother, Tom. She is looking for you. Jim, come with
me."

The other children waited until the major and Young
Jim had moved away, and then they resumed their
noisy play as if nothing had happened.

"Jim! Jim!" his father said reprovingly as they walked
across the grass toward the stables, "what is the matter
with you? Why do you always fight with Tom?"

"He wanted to be Major Beckwourth fighting the red-
coats—and that's me! That's *my* name! That's *my* right!"

His father's lips quirked in a smile, but he turned his
head so that the boy wouldn't see. Then he went on
quietly, "Yes, Jim, the name is yours by right. But not
the title of Major. That must be earned. I've noticed that
you are inclined to be jealous, Jim, of your name, of
what you think are your rights. Well, that won't do too
much harm if you learn to keep it within bounds."

He rested his hand on his son's head and his voice
grew more gentle. "You are too much like me, Jim—hot-
headed, proud, reckless. I hope you can learn, as I have
learned, to curb these feelings. You think you must always be the leader—but you cannot truly lead unless you
first learn to follow. Our great General Washington said
that, and I know it to be the truth."

Jim walked silently beside his father. Moments like
this were dear to him. Young as he was, he felt almost a
man when his father walked and talked with him. His
father, Major James Beckwourth, was the greatest man,
the bravest soldier, the finest gentleman in all the world.
Jim wanted to be exactly like his father, and he felt
proud and happy when the major admitted their resemblance, even in reproof.

"Now, Jim," Major Beckwourth went on in a more
businesslike tone, "do you think you can take a sack of

corn to the mill for me? I must have it ground today and everyone else is busy."

Young Jim's shoulders straightened. "I sure can, Pa. I'd purely like to do it."

"Very well. Have Lucius bridle Old Betsy and put a sack of corn on her back. She's gentle——"

"Too gentle, Pa. I can ride Ginger Tea——"

"You'll ride Old Betsy, or not go."

"Sure, Pa. Old Betsy's fine."

Pride filled him that Tom had not been chosen. The somber look left his black eyes and gleams of merriment danced in them. His bare feet began to dance a jig on the grass.

"Shall I start now, Pa? Right now?"

"Yes, Jim. Lucius knows what to do. Tell him I sent you."

Jim broke into a leaping run that soon carried him to the pole fence around the stable yard. This was his first man-sized job! He'd show them how well he could do it.

"Lucius!" he yelled. "Lucius!"

The old Negro came hobbling out of the barn. Jim assumed an imperious air.

"Lucius, bridle Old Betsy for me, and hoist a sack of corn onto her back. I'm taking the corn to the mill!"

"Yas, sah, Young Jim. Ah knows about dat, an' ye doan' need to put on none ob dem hoity-toity airs wif me. No, sah!" Lucius said sourly.

Jim frowned for a moment, and then suddenly his lips parted in a sunny smile and he said winningly, "Please, Lucius, hurry! I want to get going before Pa changes his mind."

Lucius responded to the smile as folks generally did

when Young Jim chose to be charming. A grin broke across his dark features.

"Yas, sah, Massa Jim! Ah sure will when you axes me lak dat. Dat's lak de Massah, hisself, dat is. He's a genneman fo' shua, an' he doan' find it necessary to be persnickity wif us folks."

Lucius led a fat old gray mare from the barn, bridled her, and led her to one side of the yard where some sacked corn lay. Stooping, the old fellow hoisted a sack and fastened it securely on the old mare's back.

"Dat's yore saddle, Young Jim," he grinned, giving the boy a leg up onto the mare's back.

"You settled all right, Massa Jim?" the old servant asked anxiously, peering up to where Jim sat perched on the corn, his feet coming only halfway down the fat animal's sides. "You safe, sure 'nuff?"

"Yea, Lucius, I'm fine! Hand me the reins and away we'll go!"

He grabbed the reins eagerly, kicked Old Betsy with his bare heels, and shouted triumphantly as the mare moved slowly ahead. Across the clearing she ambled, with Jim kicking frantically at her impervious sides.

"Look 'ee! Look 'ee!" Jim yelled at the children still playing on the grass. They stopped their game and stared at Young Jim. His head went up proudly. "Look 'ee! I'm going to the mill! I'm going to the mill all alone!"

The children shouted at him, ran along behind Betsy, tossing sticks and stones at the mare's broad flanks. "Ya! Ya! You'd better be careful! Injun will get you in them dark woods!"

Jim pretended not to hear, but he couldn't help seeing the forest looming dark and mysterious beyond the clearing. But he wasn't afraid. He was happy, happier than he had ever been. To be given a man's job, to be relied on—that was what Jim liked. He guided Old Betsy carefully into the narrow trail that wound between the trees.

The woods were noisy in the bright, early morning air. Birds chirped and chattered; small animals scurried away over the dry leaves on the ground; the trees swayed and whispered together.

"Wish I could see a bear," Jim thought as his glance darted here and there, half-hopeful, half-fearful.

Then he remembered something. Halfway to the mill was the cabin of the Kennedys. Wouldn't Jeff Kennedy be surprised to see him, Jim Beckwourth, going to the mill alone? Jeff was almost as old as Tom, but he'd never been sent through the woods alone on an errand like this. At least, Jim didn't think he had. Maybe, if Old Betsy would only step a little faster, he could stop and play awhile with Jeff and the other Kennedy children.

As he passed under a tree, Jim lifted his arm and broke off a branch. Letting the lines lie on the mare's neck, he stripped away the leaves to make himself a switch. With this he began to whack at Betsy's insensitive rump. It didn't do much good, but it made Jim feel that they were moving faster. He began to sing in time to his rhythmic switching:

> "The farmer went riding upon his gray mare,
>   Clippity, clippity, clop!
> With his daughter behind him so rosy and fair,
>   Clippity, clippity, clop!"

Suddenly Jim stopped singing and listened. The woods had become strangely silent. No longer were the birds singing; no little animals pattered over the rustling leaves; even the trees stood tall and dark and still.

"Ought to be hearin' the cattle, or Jeff hollerin' or something," Jim thought uneasily. "Must be pretty nigh the cabin by now."

The trail widened a bit and sunlight shone ahead. Jim kicked Betsy and hit her as hard as he could with the switch. The old mare shook her head and nickered uneasily. Then they came out of the woods, and the Kennedy cabin was right in front of them. Betsy stopped.

For a moment Jim stared at the cabin and the yard, not understanding what he saw. The children were all there—must be playing some sort of crazy game—they were lying on the ground in such strange positions—and with blood—and an arrow sticking out of Jeff's back——

Jim flung his hand to his mouth to hold back the scream that wanted to come. His shocked eyes moved, terrified, from one grotesque, silent figure to another. They were all there—Jeff and Mary, Curt, Hi, Lucy—all eight of them, even the baby, Daisy. And across the cabin doorstep were two larger figures—Mr. and Mrs. Kennedy, themselves.

Hardly knowing what he did, Jim tugged at Betsy's reins, whirled the mare around, and beat her with his switch. But now Betsy needed no switching. The smell of blood terrified her and she was as eager to get away from that horrid place as was Jim. The sack of corn began to slip, fell to the ground, but Jim managed to keep his seat on the broad back. Clinging to the reins, his eyes darting frantically here and there trying to see what horrible thing lurked in the shadows, Jim kept thinking, "I mustn't yell! I mustn't let them hear me!"

He was sobbing hysterically when he fell from the sweating mare's back in front of the Big House in the Beckwourth clearing. His face was putty-colored as he half-yelled, half-sobbed, "Injuns! Injuns! Injuns!"

His father came running, followed by all who were within hearing, and when Jim was able to pant out his story, Major Beckwourth went into action at once. Word was sent to all the cabins in the neighborhood; women and children were hustled into the blockhouse prudently built for just such emergencies; the men collected arms and ammunition and made ready to defend their homes. Everyone expected an attack and they knew they must be prepared.

The major, himself, with a few of the best shots among the men, went bravely to the Kennedy cabin and gave the mutilated bodies a decent burial, all the time keeping alert watch, their guns ready.

So for days the settlers waited, frightened, determined, their eyes constantly studying the woods and the river. Across the broad stream they could see flickering council fires, hear an occasional war whoop, see silhouetted dancers. But the expected attack never came. The Indians seemed to know that the desperate settlers were ready and would give no quarter. If they couldn't take the settlement by surprise, they would not risk a fight. After a time the people went back to their usual work.

But for awhile Jim was a hero. It was his warning that had saved them. The boy basked happily in the approval of his elders, and strutted before the other children.

In spite of this, Jim was puzzled. He kept asking his father, "Why did they do it? Why, Pa? The Kennedys never hurt anyone. They were good to the Injuns—gave 'em food. I've seen them. Why? Why?"

And his father's answer was always the same. "It's just Indian nature, Jim. We have to expect things like this on the frontier. The only thing to do is to be quicker than they are, more wary. Never trust them. You just have to out-Indian the Indians, that's all."

Jim shook his head and repeated slowly to himself, "Indian nature. Just out-Indian the Indian, that's all."

CHAPTER 2

Jim Grows Up

XXXXXXXXXXXXXXXXXXXXXXXXXXXXXXXXXXXXXXXXXXXXXXXXXXXXX

The games Jim and his companions liked to play took on a change in character. Instead of acting out the siege of Stony Point, and other battles the major had told them of, Jim devised a number of Indian-white man games. Sometimes the children were divided into two bands—attacking Red Men opposed by fearless whites. At other times the "Indians" hid in the forest while the "settlers" stalked them. Or the "savages" might be having a war dance around a tiny bonfire when they were attacked by a band of daring Missourians. In every game, of course, the "whites" were victorious and the "Indians" were mercilessly slaughtered.

For some time Jim chose to be leader of the white band, and as such he began to learn how to handle firearms, at first only in play. But as his father saw the boy's interest in guns and his obvious aptitude for handling arms, he decided it was time to initiate Jim into the skill that was so necessary for preservation on the frontier. Serious lessons rapidly displaced the play, and under his father's guidance, Jim became an excellent marksman. Before the year was over, he could handle his father's long Kentucky rifle by using a forked stick to hold the barrel steady.

Then, suddenly, Jim's interest veered to the bow and arrow, and he switched from playing leader of the "settlers" to the role of the Indian chieftain of the little band. There was genuine challenge in trying to outwit Tom in these games, for Tom immediately took over the leadership vacated by the younger boy. Now Jim practiced constantly with the more primitive weapon, his dark eyes shining with delight when he could strike a distant target with almost unerring success. From this time on, the battles between the two bands of children were more nearly equal, and the "savages" as often as not came off the victors.

While all this was going on, Jim was being urged along a far different course by an uncontrollable inner drive for knowledge, spurred by envy of his half brother. Tom was being taught to read and write, in preparation for going to Richmond to attend school there. Nothing had been said about sending Jim to school, but he couldn't bear to watch Tom acquire a secret knowledge of which he was ignorant.

Major Beckwourth came into the Big House one day to find Jim sitting cross-legged in a corner with the big Bible open on his knees.

"What are you doing, Jim?" his father asked curiously. It was an unusual sight to see any of the children, even Tom, interested in a book.

"How can you tell what this book says?" Jim demanded, looking up. "You read things out of it—and Tom says he can read it; so can Simon. How do you all know those things are here? How do you all get the same story? I've been studying it, and I can't see anything but little black marks. How do you know what they say?"

Major Beckwourth looked down at his son, interest bright in his eyes. This boy was not like the others on the place. That was truly an intelligent question. He sat down in a nearby chair.

"Bring the book here, Jim. Maybe I can show you a little about it."

He took the big book on his knee, and with Jim watching carefully, he gave the boy his first reading lesson.

"Each of these little black marks is a letter. There are twenty-six letters, and I'll write them out for you to learn. When the letters are put together in the right combinations they make words—and words have meaning. See—here is a short word. It has three different letters, G and O and D. Each letter has its own name and its own sound. If we sound these letters we have the word G-O-D. So it is with each of these words—"In the beginning God created the heaven and the earth." He read slowly, pointing at each word as he pronounced it.

Jim was fascinated. "I'm going to learn to read that book," he declared.

His father smiled. "I'll have Simon help you. You can take lessons right along with Tom."

So young Jim's playtime was curtailed a bit as his lessons began. Simon was the overseer on the Beckwourth place, or plantation, as the major liked to call it, remembering his Virginia home. Jim, with his desire to equal Tom spurring him on, was a remarkable student, learning rapidly and remembering well.

The year passed and the time came for Tom to be sent to his grandmother in Richmond. There he would attend school for a year, preparing for William and Mary College, where he would obtain the education his mother felt was necessary for a landed gentleman such as Tom would be.

Jim watched the preparations for Tom's departure with a sullen interest which he did not try very hard to conceal. It had been decided that Tom's mother would go with him for a long deferred visit with her family, and the resulting arrangements required the attention of nearly everyone on the place. But at last the travelers with their servants were gone to make the long perilous journey by boat and stagecoach.

No sooner was order restored on the plantation than Jim presented himself before his father.

"I want to go to school, too," he announced without preamble. "Simon says I'm ready for a real school."

Major Beckwourth smiled at the boy. "And where, pray, will you find this school? I have seen none hereabouts."

"Simon says there's a new school in St. Louis. You could take me down when you make your trip to the city this fall."

His father studied the boy speculatively, a frown of concentration in his brow. "I'm afraid you don't know what you're asking, Jim, I don't think you'd care for school."

"Why wouldn't I?" Jim demanded.

"You're not of a disposition to take kindly to the restraints of a schoolroom."

"Tom's going to school," Jim couldn't help saying.

"Yes," his father answered patiently, "but you know Tom has a different disposition than yours. And Tom has relatives to look after him while he is away. In St. Louis you'd be alone——"

"I wouldn't care. I'm not afraid——"

"Of course not. But the main thing, Jim, is that I am sure you'd be unhappy. You do not like to be ordered around. You are headstrong and proud. These things make for trouble in a school."

Jim was not convinced by his father's argument, and day after day he returned to the question until at last Major Beckwourth gave in. By the time he was ready for his regular fall trip to St. Louis he had decided to try the experiment of putting Young Jim in the new school at St. Louis, established only this year, and the first school in all of Missouri. The major was still dubious about the success of the venture, yet he hoped that the routine of school life would tame the spirit of this unusual boy. His son had great possibilities, if his talents could only be directed into the right channels.

Major Beckwourth was to find his hope too optimistic, and Young Jim was to find the restraints of school life galling to his independent spirit. He learned with amazing rapidity and ease and often outshone his more fortunately situated classmates. Especially in sports and games, Jim's skill and prowess made him too often a victor. This in turn created envy and jealousy in the defeated boys, and Jim was too young, too eager to prove his equality to know how to handle the troubles that arose. Major Beckwourth's money and position could get Jim into the school, but it could not control the reactions of the boys. And Jim relied too often upon his fists to punish those who, in defeat and anger, shouted slurs upon his birth and his parentage.

The patient Jesuit fathers seemed to understand the turbulence of Young Jim's nature, and did everything they could to bring him into conformity with his classmates. For four long years they labored with Jim's truculence, and then, finding it impossible to change him, they requested him to leave.

"He is wholly unsuited to school life," the Jesuit Father in charge explained to Major Beckwourth. "He isn't a bad boy—not in the usual sense. But he is extremely sensitive about his situation and this makes him abnormally eager to prove that he is not only the equal, but the superior, of everyone with whom he comes into contact. He carries a chip on his shoulder and dares the world to knock it off. There may be a place somewhere for this boy, but it is not in an institution."

At fourteen, now, Jim was a large boy, with a compact, athletic build and strong, aquiline features set off by fine dark eyes. One thing, however, marred what would otherwise have been a most attractive countenance. Jim's mouth, which could smile winningly, generally wore a sullen expression which became bitterly resentful if the boy had a notion that anyone was condescending toward him. With trusted friends he would melt into warm and gentle ways; but for the most part his whole attitude was arrogant and domineering.

Disappointed that Jim had not responded to school life, Major Beckwourth was now faced with the problem of finding something for this talented, stubborn son to do. He knew that Jim would not fit into life on the plantation. His half brother Tom, nearly eighteen and finished with college, would have little patience with the arrogance and insubordination of the younger boy. On the other hand, Jim would never submit to Tom's domination. There would be nothing but friction and possible tragedy. The only thing to do, the major decided ruefully, was to apprentice Jim to some trade in St. Louis.

The major had much of his blacksmith work done at a shop run by George Casner and John Sutton. He liked Casner, and knew him for a man of strength and authority. He was an honest workman, whose integrity Jim would have to respect. The major approached the blacksmith with his proposition, and Casner readily agreed to take Jim on as an apprentice. He really liked the boy, who had often visited the shop with his father, and had showed a great liking for horses.

"He's a bit obstreperous," Major Beckwourth observed tentatively.

"Don't let it worry ye none, sir!" Casner said stoutly. "I like a younker to hev spirit, I do. An' if it gits out o' bounds, I'm the man kin bring it to heel, sir!"

Looking at the smith's muscled arms and firm jaw, the major agreed and the affair was settled.

Beckwourth lost no time in acquainting Young Jim with the arrangement. "And it makes little difference what your feelings are in the matter," he said sternly. "Apprenticed you are and apprenticed you shall be, and work out your time with Casner. And let me tell you, sirrah, if you run away or cause any trouble, I shall not step in to save you. The law shall take its course, and you very well know what that course is—you'll be brought back in chains and imprisoned if necessary to force you to submission. If you are irked by the restraints of learning an honest trade, consider the restraint of chains and prison bars." Then, relenting a bit at the look on his son's face, he said more gently, "You must learn to be a man, Jim. You must learn to stand by yourself in this world—and that means not treading on others' toes, any more than you permit them to tread on yours. I've had a great deal of trouble with you, Jim, and a great deal of patience. Now I must prepare you, somehow, to make your own way."

At first Casner found the boy rebellious and difficult, but gradually the smith's firmness and cheerfulness won Jim over to a fair degree of cooperation. Moreover, Jim found that he liked the work. He liked horses, liked to handle them, though he often lost patience with a stupid or stubborn animal. And he enjoyed the feeling of power that came from shaping iron to his will. As he slung the heavy hammer against the glowing metal on the anvil, his spirits rose, and he felt strong and happy.

Another thing that pleased Jim was that he was ac-cepted as an equal among the young men that hung about the taverns or loafed on the street corners. These young fellows were men, and it made Jim's ego glow to be taken for one of them. In order to amuse the others and to do his part in entertaining these loafers, Jim learned a number of tricks, perfected his wrestling and fighting techniques, and tried in every way to show that he was as much a man as any of them.

One trick that always won the attention of the crowd was Jim's ability to hold two horseshoes together in his hands, and by sheer muscular power, force the two ends toward each other until they met, or pull them apart until the iron was almost straight. Some of the other fellows were strong enough to do this with one horse-shoe, but only Jim could manage it with two together.

For two or three years Jim was rather contented and happy at the blacksmith shop, and his father, on his visits to St. Louis, began to feel that his troubles with Jim were over. And then Jim began to grow restless. He abused the freedom Casner allowed him, and grew more and more resentful of any attempt to make him toe the mark. He stayed out late at night, and appeared at the shop only when he felt like it. He neglected his work to go fishing or hunting, or to loaf around the taverns, wrestling or fighting, and listening to the tales he heard there.

There were always men with tall tales to tell: rough trappers down from the little-known Upper Missouri, who brought in peltries to build up the fortunes of Manuel Lisa or the wealthy Chouteaus. When the ele-gant Chouteau carriage went flying past the tavern, spraying dust on the onlookers, these bearded trappers would spit a stream of tobacco juice and begin a yarn. It was due to them that the Chouteaus lived in their elegant rock house, had dozens of black servants, and rode in gold-trimmed carriages. There was money in furs, but not for the man who braved the Indians and the cold and hunger and thirst of the wilderness. No. The money was for those who stayed snugly at home and let others win it for them.

Jim, listening, his keen intelligence working behind those bright, dark eyes, would shake his head. If the trappers were only smart—smart as Chouteau and Lisa —they would be able to get hold of some of that wealth for themselves. And he would look down the sloping, cobbled street to the wharf, where keelboats lay waiting to carry bands of trappers up the treacherous Missouri to bring back more furs to add more wealth to those aristocrats of the city. As he looked, Jim would grow discontented with the dull routine of the blacksmith shop, with its lusterless future, its total lack of promise. Tom, he would think bitterly, had his fortune made already. Jim must make his own, and he could never do it at Casner's.

By the time he was nineteen, Jim was taller than his boss, he was muscular and agile, clever at wrestling and fighting, and considered the best marksman in his crowd of cronies, all of them tough and skillful fighters. His natural arrogance was aggravated by his popularity with youths of his own age. He looked at Casner, who could neither read nor write, and who tallied his accounts on his ten fingers, and he was filled with disgust that he, Jim Beckwourth, was bound to serve this man. He took scant pains to hide his contempt from his boss.

Casner, on the other hand, was growing increasingly

weary of his apprentice's irresponsibility and shiftless-
ness. The cheery tolerance he had shown to the fourteen-
year-old gave way to bitter impatience with the young
man. Casner's respect for the major was the only thing
that kept him from administering the physical punishment any employer was entitled to give an insubordinate
apprentice.

At last, his patience at an end, the blacksmith decided
to terminate the intolerable situation. Jim would behave
or suffer the consequences. With this determination,
Casner waited impatiently one day for Jim's arrival at
the smithy. As the morning grew old, his irritation
mounted.

Finally, about noon, Young Jim came sauntering into
the shop, yawning and rumpled. Casner stopped his work
and stared at the youth. Then all his pent-up resentment
flared forth in a stream of oaths and reproof. As Jim
stood, hands on hips, staring insolently at the man,
Casner shouted, "Ye'll obey me, or I'll beat obedience
into ye! Hear that! There's work to be done, and ye'll
do it! Now pick up thet hammer and git to work, or
ye'll feel the weight o' me fist aginst yer brash face, ye
lazy, good-fer-nothing runagate!"

Jim smiled coolly, but hot lights were dancing in his
dark eyes. "I take no orders addressed to me in that
language!" he said, taking care to use the most cultivated
tone and words he could master in order to emphasize
his superiority over the irate smith. "As for your filthy
hammer, pick it up and use it yourself. You can't tell
me what I shall and shall not do!"

"Use it, that I will!" shouted Casner, and grabbing the
heavy hammer from the bench, flung it straight at Jim's
insolent face.

Jim dodged, caught the hammer almost before it touched the floor, and flung it back at the blacksmith.

It missed Casner, who came leaping toward his helper, growling like a maddened bull, his head down, his huge hands reaching for Jim. Immediately they were locked in a desperate struggle, each one so lost to reason that he wished only to stop the other forever. Back and forth across the littered shop they struggled, but Jim, being younger and more agile than his master, before long had Casner on the floor, and was kneeling on his chest.

"I could finish the job right now," Jim panted, "but I won't. I well know what would happen to me, a mere apprentice, no matter what my aggravation might be. No, I'm going to let you up," and he jerked Casner to his feet, "and give you a chance to dismiss me from your service. I'm not going to run away—my father warned me against that, and many a time that warning has kept me here when my feet were itching to get away. Dismiss me, I say!" He shook the big man angrily.

Casner stood silent, his face black with anger and hatred. Jim gave him another shake. "Tell me I'm dismissed from your service!"

Seeing there was no escape, Casner muttered the desired words. Immediately Jim flung him aside, turned on his heel and left the shop.

He went to his boardinghouse to pack up his belongings and get far away before Casner could start any reprisal. As he packed, he heard voices downstairs, and, going to the door to listen, he recognized the voice of Clements, the one-armed constable, demanding to know where Jim was. So that was it! Casner was going to have him arrested for assault, or for running away, or for any other charge he might wish to bring. There was only one chance of escaping arrest. That was to get out of the house, make it to the river, and get onto the boat he knew was ready to move upstream in the morning.

Taking his bundle in one hand and a gun in the other, Jim started slowly down the stairs. The constable looked up, into the muzzle of Jim's well-aimed pistol.

"Don't try to stop me, Clements!" Jim said quietly. "If you do, I'll fill you full of lead."

Jim's reputation for marksmanship and for recklessness was well known. Constable Clements stood still, his hand holding a pistol dropped to his side. Silently, he watched Jim walk across the room and out of the door.

Once outside, Jim lost no time in hurrying down the cobbled street to the wharf. Running to the keelboat tied there, with men busy about its decks preparing for the early departure, Jim leaped onto the low deck and hurried to the captain.

"I want to go upriver with you, sir," he said urgently. "I have money for my passage, or I can work my way as hunter for your men. I'm Jim Beckwourth—and can guarantee fresh meat for you every day of your trip."

The captain looked him over and grinned. "Running away, eh? Well, Beckwourth, I don't give a hoot about your private affairs. I've heard of you and I know you're about the best hunter in these parts. And a good hunter I can use. I'll take you on."

Jim's sudden, charming smile broke across his face. "And will you let me stay aboard until you leave tomorrow? I'd rather not be seen about the streets."

The captain chuckled. "Sure! Sure! Take your bundle and get inside the deckhouse."

Jim turned to pick up his bundle, and came face to face with Casner, who was pointing a pistol straight at his heart.

"No ye don't," growled the blacksmith. "Ye ain't goin' to run away like a scairt rabbit. I know yore pa. I promised him I'd hold onto ye, an' hold on I will till he comes hisself an' sez to let go. Pick up yer bundle an' march!"

Jim shrugged. He knew only too well there was no use arguing with a loaded gun. Turning his back on river and boat, shouldering his bundle, he marched slowly up the street down which he had so recently come running with high hope.

CHAPTER 3

The Gaudy Liar

XXXXXXXXXXXXXXXXXXXXXXXXXXXXXXXXXXXXXXXXXXXXXXXXXXX

Blacksmith Casner marched Jim straight to the hotel on Front Street where, he had learned, Major Beckwourth had arrived that morning. At his truculent demand to see the major, he was shown immediately into a small parlor, where Jim's father sat reading.

"Here's yore son, sir!" the blacksmith began caustically. "Runnin' away he were. Runnin' away on a river boat after tryin' to give me, his master, a drubbin'. But, I ketched him and fotched him back here to ye, sir. I knowed ye'd do the right thing by me an' by him, too, sir!" he ended meaningfully.

"Leave him to me, Casner," the major ordered sharply, and the blacksmith, frowning, had no choice but to leave the room and forgo the pleasure of watching Jim's punishment.

The major, who had already heard of the fight in the blacksmith shop, was more disappointed than angry with his son.

"What is going to happen to you, Jim?" he asked. "You know the punishment for runaway apprentices. I warned you——"

Jim's dark eyes glowed sullenly, but he gave no answer. It would do no good, he was thinking, to put him in jail. They could not keep him in chains forever, and when the chains were removed, he would escape, some-

33

how. He knew for a certainty that life with Casner would be utterly unbearable.

"I want you to go back to Casner and finish out your term as apprentice," his father said sternly. "There is less than a year left."

Jim's head jerked up proudly. His black eyes looked straight into his father's. "Never!" he said. "I'll never go back."

The major didn't argue. He knew that subborn streak too well. And he didn't know what epithet Casner might, in his rage, have cast at this haughty youth. It might have been, Beckwourth was thinking, something that Jim could not bring himself to repeat. He had warned Jim that he would not rescue him from any difficulty he might get into. But he couldn't abide by that decision. There was not only the bond of blood—there was the stronger bond of similar personalities, of deep and true affection.

At last the major said quietly, "Well, then, I'll pay Casner off, and you can come back home and start a business of some sort. I reckon you know enough about blacksmithing——"

Jim's eyes softened at his father's reasonableness. It was more than he had dared to hope for. The surly look gave way to one of tenderness for this understanding father. Still Jim felt he must refuse the offer.

"No, Pa," he said quietly. "Thanks for the offer, but it would not work, not with Tom there——"

The major sighed resignedly. "What is it you want then, Jim? What will you do with yourself? I don't want a son of mine running wild."

Jim had the answer to that. "I want to make money, to get rich, have people look up to me, to make my name known as yours is—and I can do it, too. But not as a blacksmith," he ended bitterly. Then he went on with enthusiasm, "There are fortunes being made up North, Pa, and out West—fortunes in furs. The Chouteaus, Manuel Lisa—they've become rich and famous but they haven't scratched the surface of the fortunes hidden away in the wilds where no one has ever been. And not only furs—there are the mines—people digging riches right out of the earth." His voice became passionate. "Why should the Indians and a few white men have it all? Let me go out—away from this miserable little town, away from bosses and constables. Let me go out where I can be free to be myself!"

The major was silent for a long moment, studying the dark eyes, the intelligent features, the tall, powerful young body. Jim was a man already, although he was only nineteen. He should be permitted a man's choice of life and livelihood.

"All right, Jim," his father said at last. "You may go where you please, do as you please. But I trust you not to disgrace the name I have bestowed upon you."

Jim, always emotional, was almost overcome by his father's capitulation. He grasped his father's hand, and tears stood in his eyes as he said with a trembling voice, "Thank you, Father. I am glad that we part as friends——"

"More than friends, my son," the major said, his voice also filled with emotion. "And you shall not go penniless. Not only will I pay off Casner, but I'll give you money enough to save you from menial service, protect you from starvation if your plans go awry." He hesitated a moment, thinking, and then went on, "Colonel Johnson is starting upriver tomorrow on a peaceable mission to the Indians that own the lead mines up North. He is to make a treaty with the Sauk and the Fox tribes so that the white man can work the lead mines without fear. If you'd like to start out with him, I'll talk to him tonight. I know him well, and have no doubt I can secure a berth for you with him."

Jim's eyes glowed. "Yes, I would like that. It would be a chance for me to find out whether the mines are for me."

Jim was delighted. While his father soothed and paid off the blacksmith and made arrangements with Colonel Johnson, Jim went happily about the taverns bidding his cronies good-by. And the picture he painted of his prospects was not a dull one, by any means.

The next morning, instead of having to sneak aboard like a fugitive, Jim boarded the colonel's keelboat amid the noisy good-bys of his friends. Major Beckwourth, too, was there to give his son an encouraging word of farewell, hand him a leather poke filled with money, and, at the very last, to throw his arm about the shoulder of his rebellious son and bid him Godspeed.

The trip upriver was like a holiday for Jim. At the very beginning, Colonel Johnson appointed him hunter for the officer's own mess. This not only relieved Jim of much arduous work on the boat, but gave him some prestige; he was in the preferred boat of the ten that made up the flotilla. Jim was flattered, too, because the colonel's son, Darwin, a youth of seventeen, attached himself to the hunter with an admiration and awe that was balm to Jim's troubled ego.

It was impossible to navigate after dark, so at sundown each day the boats were brought to shore and camp made for the night. And sitting with his companions around the campfire, Jim discovered that he possessed a knack that was even more prized than his skill as a hunter. Jim was a born storyteller, as he had discovered in the taverns and on the street corners of St. Louis. But this was different. Here in the romantic setting of the night camp, with the forest dark and mysterious around them, and not knowing what dangers lurked in the shadows, he was stimulated to make up all sorts of daring tales. His audience was eager and credulous, drinking in the tall tales and clamoring for more. Jim, embroidering each story with all the art of his active imagination, felt thoroughly repaid when the men crowded around, slapped him on the back and chortled, "Gar! What a gaudy liar! Ain't never been sech a liar on this here old river!"

The Gaudy Liar! Jim grinned to himself. It was the first title of honor ever bestowed upon him by white comrades.

The three weeks passed so pleasantly that Jim was almost sorry when Indian huts along the shore showed that they had come to the end of their journey. Word of the approaching expedition had, as usual, preceded the boats, and the Indians were lined up in colorful array to greet the newcomers. Behind a row of brilliantly costumed braves, the women and children crowded in a higgledy-piggledy mass, with mangy yellow dogs leaping and yelping among them.

Jim noticed that there was a good deal of variety in the costuming and painting of the braves, but Darwin explained that many tribes were present.

"We're supposed to treat with the Sauk and Fox," he said, proud to display his knowledge of Indian affairs, "but other tribes have heard about the parley and come in to share in the gifts and the expected distribution of food and rum. Those fellows with the high, bushy roach of hair are Foxes. That bunch naked to the waist are Potawatamies. And over there in those painted and beaded buckskin shirts are some Sauk warriors. Each tribe has its own peculiar way of painting their bodies and wearing their hair."

Seeing the braves with their fearsome, painted faces and their ceremonial dress trimmed with shanks of hair that he suddenly realized were scalps, Jim felt a shiver of apprehension. There before him in vivid detail he seemed to see the Kennedy family lying in the clearing before their cabin. They had been killed and mutilated by savages such as these. His hands tightened instinctively on his gun, and a brutal desire for revenge sent the blood ringing to his head.

For a moment he reeled dizzily before he could gain command of himself. Then he looked about quickly, but no one seemed to have noticed his agitation. All eyes were focused upon one man. He was a tall Indian, his face and body painted black, his limbs decorated with wide white stripes. A tall feather headdress, feather kneelets and anklets, and a spear shaft decorated with colored feathers gave to this chieftain a wild and savage look.

"That's Keokuck!" whispered Darwin. "I saw him at the parley at Portage des Sioux last spring."

Jim stared at this chieftain, known throughout the whole Mississippi region as one friendly to the Americans, while his rival, Black Hawk, favored the British. Jim was astonished to see silken British flags flying from spear shafts along with the Stars and Stripes of his own country, but Darwin whispered, "Look at that! The British got into this region before us, and gave the Indians those flags to bind their allegiance to England. My

father has urged and urged our government to distribute
our flags, but so far only a few have been given out."

Colonel Johnson, flanked by his officers, was advancing to greet Keokuck with the greatest ceremony. After
the preliminary exchange of courtesies, the officers were
led into the council lodge. Keokuck and his chief men
also entered the long bark structure, and the lesser men
of both groups were left outside to do as they pleased.

Almost immediately, games were started—foot races,
target shooting with bow and arrow, jumping, and feats
of prowess. The Indians, several of whom could speak
some English, invited the colonel's men to join in the
sport.

For a time Jim stook back, watching. One handsome
Potawatami brave seemed to be winning everything,
and Jim felt a secret urge to try his skill against that of
the Indian. Darwin, who had been Jim's companion on
many a day's hunt and who had a great respect for
Jim's marksmanship, gave his companion a poke.

"Step up, Jim! Show him what you can do!"

Others of the party took up the cry. "Go ahead, Jim!
Here's yore chance to vindicate the white man!" they
yelled, pushing Jim forward.

Shabona, the Potawatami, stood waiting, bow in
hand, for some one to challenge him in the target shoot.
He looked cool and arrogant as Jim, encouraged by the
cheers of his companions, stepped forward and accepted
a bow and arrow from a watching Sauk. Some sixty paces
away a cornstalk had been fastened upright in the
ground as a target. Shabona gave one calm glance at
Jim, stepped to the line and raised his bow. There was
the whang of the bowstring as the Indian's arrow was
sent flying. Jim's eyes followed the feathered shaft. The
flint arrowhead struck the target fairly in the middle

and remained there, the feathered haft quivering as if alive.

Jim pretended an ease he did not feel, although he was confident that with his own familiar weapons he could match the Indian's shot. However, he fitted the arrow against the bowstring, raised his arm, and took careful aim.

A cheer rose from both the white and the Indian on-lookers as Jim's arrow cleanly cut Shabona's feathered shaft. For a moment consternation clouded the Potawatami's features, then an appreciative grin wiped away all trace of discomfiture. He grunted approvingly.

The ice broken, Johnson's men joined in the sports with vigor, sometimes winning, sometimes losing a contest. But they were not ashamed of their showing, and it was evident that Jim's skill and strength had completely captivated their Indian hosts.

From this moment on, Shabona was Jim's friend. As the parley dragged on day after day, the Potawatami showed his "brother" the best places to hunt and fish so that the colonel's men never lacked a hearty supper.

Jim enjoyed the freedom and prestige of his new situation, and when Colonel Johnson was ready to return to St. Louis, Jim had decided to stay in the North. The treaty had been signed, the mines were humming, and Jim was assured of plenty of employment either as a miner or as a hunter.

There were only a handful of white men in the entire lead region, just a few hundred, while the Indian workers numbered in the thousands. Jim found that he enjoyed working with the Indians, and that he possessed some knack that made it easy for him to get along with them.

Jim spent a year and a half here on the Upper Mississippi, working most of the time as a hunter. Occasionally, tempted by the excellent pay, he went down into the mines. But he detested the backbreaking, confining work, and would soon give it up for the freedom of the woods and streams.

At the end of eighteen months his poke was filled with gold and he decided to return to St. Louis. Now he could swagger along the streets of the city, stand treat in the taverns, and gather avid audiences with his tales of adventure in the northern wilds. So he bade Shabona good-by, boarded a boat carrying lead to St. Louis, and set out for home.

CHAPTER 4

An Ashley Man

XXXXXXXXXXXXXXXXXXXXXXXXXXXXXXXXXXXXXXXXXXXXXXXXXXXXXXXXXXX

St. Louis proved a disappointment to the gaudy liar of the wilderness. Many of his old friends had married and settled down to a staid life that did not permit loafing around taverns to listen to Jim's elaborate yarns. Some had left on adventures of their own. The streets and taverns had lost much of their glamour.

Jim made a short visit to his father's settlement below St. Charles, now called Beckwourth's Settlement and a thriving community. He found his father perceptibly older, troubled by illness. The management of the place had been handed entirely to Tom, who showed little of his father's easygoing treatment of the workers, and ran the place as the aristocratic Virginia gentleman he fancied himself. Toward Jim he displayed a haughty disdain that was meant to put his half brother "in his place."

Jim pretended not to notice Tom's attiude, but there was one thing he couldn't ignore. His sisters, Matilda and Louise, were desperately unhappy in their situation as slaves under Tom's management. Jim went to his father.

"I'm leaving here," he said shortly, "and don't know when, if ever, I'll be back. But before I go, there is one thing I want you to do, Pa. I want you to give Matilda and Louise their freedom. They want to go to St. Louis to live, away from here, where they can earn a decent living as free women. Will you do that one thing for me? It is all I'll get as an inheritance!" he finished bitterly.

Major Beckwourth nodded. "I'll do it, son," he promised. His tired eyes surveyed the tall, stalwart young fellow, the very image of himself when he had joined the Bluecoats so long ago. He sighed. "If I were only young again, Jim, I'd go with you. You'll find adventure and excitement, somewhere. Here," he waved his hand in a weary gesture, "here the frontier is conquered. Life stands still."

Back in St. Louis again, Jim heard rumors which sent him to the office of General William H. Ashley. He was ushered into the officer's presence and found himself facing a large man with a ruddy face and keen blue eyes.

"I hear you're looking for men to go to the mountains," Jim began without preamble. "I'd like to sign up with you."

General Ashley studied the tall dark young man before him. His memory for faces was excellent and he was trying to recall where he had seen this young fellow. In a moment he remembered, for Casner's shop had often been patronized by the officer. And he had heard of the fight which had resulted in the disappearance of the smith's capable helper.

"Weren't you an apprentice to Casner, the blacksmith?" Ashley asked. "Wasn't there some trouble with your master?"

The word "master" was one Jim could not endure. He drew himself up proudly. "I was apprenticed to Casner as a boy," he said. "But I am now free, and a man, and can go where I wish, and do as I wish."

The general shook his head. "No need to get on your high horse, young man. What experience have you had?

What makes you think you can be of service to me?"

"I've spent eighteen months in Indian country—up at the lead mines. I've learned that I can parley with them and handle them well. I'm a good hunter—the best in St. Louie," he added calmly.

A wry smile twisted the general's lips and he said dryly, "You speak your piece well, young man. And I'm inclined to accept you at your own value. I just hope that you've learned to control that temper that got you into trouble with Casner. I want no hotheads among my men. I am sending expeditions into the mountains, far beyond the usual range of trappers. It is dangerous business and requires coolness and good judgment more than anything else."

The general's right hand drummed on the table while his shrewd eyes went over Jim's figure. Then, making a quick decision, he went on, "I'm in desperate need of a daring man. I'll outline my proposition to you and then, if you still wish to enter my employ, I'll sign you on. Sit down and listen."

Jim took a seat. He kept his dark eyes on the shrewd blue eyes of the officer as he listened with interest.

"Up till now," the general explained, "the fur traders and trappers have relied on the rivers for transportation. They have been limited, therefore, to valleys accessible to the Mississipppi, the Missouri, and the Yellowstone. But there are other rivers and lakes, rich in possibilities, that have not been touched.

"One of these is the Platte. It's a thousand miles long and six inches deep, they say," Ashley grinned, "and boats cannot be used on it. Nevertheless, the valley of the Platte offers the easiest road to the mountains. Horses are the answer. With horses I can follow the Platte to the mountains, cross the Divide, and come upon other streams and lakes that have not yet been explored. My partner, Andrew Henry, has traversed much of this country, and he assures me there are beaver on these streams. Now, I already have some parties in the mountains, but they are in need of more horses. I want to recruit a small band of men to go with me to the Pawnee villages on the Arkansas to purchase animals which I can send to the mountains."

The excitement in Jim's eyes died. "But I want to go to the mountains!" he exclaimed. "I thought if I joined your company that's where I'd be sent."

"In good time," Ashley answered. "If you serve me well, you'll get to the mountains. At present, this job is all I can offer."

"Very well, sir!" Jim agreed, "I'll take it."

General Ashley's horse-buying expedition set out in October. Everything went smoothly until the party reached the village of the Kansas Indians on the river named for that tribe. There the general suffered one of the periodic setbacks that had dogged his ventures ever since he sent out his first band of men early in 1822. He awoke one morning to find that all his horses were gone —spirited away in the night by the adroit red men.

Ashley called a council. "We can't get very far on the prairies without horses," he observed glumly, "and it is getting too late in the year to try to replenish our stock and then go on with my plan. I think the best thing for me to do is to return to St. Louis for this winter. You men can return, also, if you wish.

"However, I would like to send a couple of men to the Pawnees on the Republican River. These Indians are willing to sell horses, and my men can purchase a band and bring them back to St. Louis. Two men can subsist and get through where a large party would perish.

Now," he looked about him, "who will volunteer to undertake this mission? I will not hide from you the fact that it is a perilous one—and only the bravest and hardiest need offer."

He looked around at the bearded faces, but no eye met his and no man stepped forward. At last his eyes fell on Moses Harris, called Black by his comrades. Harris was a great hulk of a man, with bushy black hair, beard and eyebrows. He was noted for his strength and his great powers of walking, and for his tall tales. He had been in General Ashley's employ for two years now, having been one of that first, select group sent out by the general in the spring of '22.

"Harris," Ashley said now, "you are a man I know well —I've tested your strength and endurance before now. Will you go to the Pawnees for me?"

Black Harris spat a stream of brown tobacco juice through his beard. "Gar, General!" he said, "ye picked the right child this time, wagh! Sure enough I'll go, ef ye kin pick me one good man to keep up with me."

"Good! And now for a companion." The general's eyes moved on to where Jim stood among the others. "You, Beckwourth! Do you think you are capable of undertaking a task like this?"

The way the general phrased the question irked Jim. Without stopping to consider what it might mean, he answered, "I'm capable of any task that any other man can take on."

Ashley smiled with satisfaction. It was easy enough to handle a man like Jim Beckwourth. He'd do anything that others doubted he could do—or that he thought others doubted.

"You're loony!" whispered Basil, one of the men with whom Jim had become rather friendly. "Your'e loony,

Jim. The Pawnees are three hundred miles away and
winter's coming on. Black Harris is a man of great leg,
but you're new to the plains. If you fall behind, he'll
leave you to perish, while he goes on to save his own
skin."

Jim nodded appreciation of his friend's council, but
said, "I'm a man of great leg, too. But if I do fall behind,
he'd better not leave me."

As they were getting ready to set out, Black Harris
couldn't resist trying to tease his companion. After all,
Jim was a "manger du lard"—a pork-eater—newcomer,
while Black was an old hand. He had traveled "express"
several times, and such a trip, with but one companion,
was nothing new to him.

"Well, younker," he said, "ye think ye kin keep up
with this child? Wagh! Ye'll hev some leg if ye kin!"

Jim looked up coolly. "I don't know whether I can
keep up or not, but I'll tell you this, Black. You leave me
to perish alone and by heaven, if I can raise up on one
arm, I'll shoot—and shoot to stop you in your tracks!"

Black grinned insolently, "Ye will, will ye? Well now
I'll tell ye what I'll do, jest to show ye this child's fair an'
square. I'll let ye step out ahead, and ye kin take yore
own jog. Then, if ye give out 'twill be yore own fault, an'
not this here child's. An' if ye fall by the way, this child
will do whatsomever he thinks best, an' ye kin take it er
leave it. Wagh!"

The next morning Jim and Black Harris set out on
foot to try to make it to the Pawnee village. Each man
carried enough provisions to last him, along with what
game he could kill, until he reached the Indians. In addition, each had a blanket, his gun, and ammunition.

Harris, as good as his word, placed Jim ahead of him on

the trail, so the less experienced man could "take his own jog." Eager to distinguish himself, Jim set out at a rather fast clip. The trail was flat and not difficult, and the two strode along, saying little. When the sun was directly overhead they nooned and rested a little and started on again.

As the afternoon wore on Jim began to feel the strain of the unusual exercise, but not for anything would he cry halt. As his weariness grew, he gritted his teeth and kept doggedly on, hoping that Black would call quits. What the older man was thinking as he trudged along behind, Jim had no way of telling. But he knew that he, himself, would drop in his tracks before he would admit that he was tired.

The sun slanted lower and lower, throwing shadows longer and longer behind them. Jim's legs could scarcely take the strides he was demanding of them. Then suddenly Black let out a roar.

"Hey, thar, younker! What's the matter with yore eyesight, eh? Here's a danged good place to make a halt fer the night, an' yore prancin' right past it. Wagh!"

Jim, who had been keeping his eyes straight ahead, now glanced aside and saw a clump of trees and a small stream. It was, as Black said, a good place to stop for the night, and Jim thankfully turned toward it. He was too tired to twit Black with being the one to mention stopping, and as he looked at the big man, seemingly as fresh as when he started out, Jim knew there was little sense in saying anything. But when he told about this trip he could say that Black was first to halt—and Black couldn't gainsay it.

They dropped their packs, and Black sat down beside his, obviously expecting Jim to make the fire for their evening meal. Jim felt rebellious, but he wasn't going to give Black any cause for saying that he was a tenderfoot. So he went sullenly about the task.

As he was putting on the coffee Jim heard a shot and whirled. There sat Harris, quietly reloading his gun, which no mountaineer ever left empty for a moment.

"Thar's a dead turkey over thar fer our supper, wagh!" Black said casually, nodding toward one of the trees.

Jim started over to pick up the bird when another shot rang out and another turkey fell from the tree almost at his feet. This second bird was so fat that it burst as it hit the ground.

Jim was somewhat abashed. He had been too weary to notice the turkeys and, expert hunter though he was, he had let the other man provide the meal. But he was grateful for the food, and the two ate heartily.

After supper they killed two more turkeys and roasted them over the coals to carry on their journey. Then they rolled into their blankets and slept.

In this way the two companions hastened as fast as possible toward the Pawnee village on the Republican River. And each day Jim kept doggedly on until Black suggested stopping. Jim felt, at times, that the older man was having a bit of sport with him, letting him travel on and on until almost dark, some days. But his stubborn pride wouldn't let him give in, and day by day his muscles hardened until it was no hardship to walk from sunup to past sundown with only a brief midday rest.

With such rugged persistence did the two men travel that they reached the Republican in just ten days. But there was no Indian village here—only the scattered debris that told where a village had been.

"Wagh!" Black Harris spat. "Ef they haven't picked

up an' gone! Gone south to their winter hunting grounds, I reckon! Not a hide nor hair of man nor beast—no horses fer the gen'ral—an' no food fer us. Gar, this child is plumb licked!"

Jim was as discouraged as his companion, but he knew there was no use in stopping here.

"I guess we'll have to go back——"

"This child votes to go on—ef we keep goin' we kin find some Injuns——"

"But that's going into unknown territory, with no food, and no telling what we'll find."

They argued it over and finally Jim won out.

"Wal, then, younker," Black conceded, "let's try to make the Ne-mah-haw River. We kin make us a raft an' float down to the Missouri an' then down that to home!"

The two set out toward where Black said they would find the Nemaha, a tributary of the Missouri. They found little game and scarcely any water. Famished and nearly dead of thirst they staggered on until, when Jim was almost sure they could go no further, they met a friendly band of Pawnee Indians, who took the two half-dead travelers to their village. There they were fed and rested.

When they were able to travel again, Black was determined to go west, while Jim was equally determined to get back to St. Louis.

"I don't blame ye none, younker," Black said reasonably. "This has been yore first experience gittin' lost on the plains. But, ef ye ever git to the mountings, ye kin expect this to happen most any time. But if ye are bent on gitting back to St. Louie, go ahead. This child is goin' out whar he knows he'll find trappers er Injuns."

So they parted company, and all alone, Jim traveled

eastward. He finally made it to the Chouteau trading post on the Upper Missouri, and there he stopped. It was too far to go on to St. Louis this winter, and Chouteau was glad to hire an able-bodied man to pack and stack the peltries brought in by the Indian trappers.

As soon as the warm spring sun melted the ice in the river so that vessels could travel, Jim set out with one of the boats carrying a rich cargo of furs for the Chouteaus. He reached St. Louis one balmy spring day, and started at once up the cobbled street to General Ashley's office. He wanted to report how it had happened that he had failed in his first mission for the general.

He got about halfway to the general's headquarters when he heard his name called. Turning, he saw General Ashley hurrying toward him from a side street.

"Jim Beckwourth, is that you!" Ashley asked, coming up. He seemed genuinely pleased to see his employe, and Jim soon understood why. "I'd given you up as lost! Where's Moses Harris? What happened to you? Come! Come up to the house and tell me all about it." And taking Jim's arm, the general hurried him along.

Jim, who had often enough during the past winter wondered how he would tell this man that he had failed to carry out his first mission, found that he needn't have worried. Ashley was so glad to find out that he was alive that he made little to-do over the lack of horses.

"I hope Harris is safe, and, if you, a new man, made it through all right, I guess I don't need to worry about Moses. But do you still wish to work for me, Beckwourth? If you do, I have another job for you. I was just looking for someone——"

When Jim nodded, the general went on, "I sent out

another expedition last week—120 good men—but I didn't have all the cash on hand that they'll need. I promised to send more—and I want you to ride with all speed and carry this money to Tom Fitzpatrick. Can you do that? They are only six days ahead of you. If you ride fast you can soon overtake them."

Jim was glad to find he was still in Ashley's good graces, as he must be to be trusted with a large sum of money. He had been worried, he admitted to himself, about what his reception would be. The general was noted for his quick temper and his impatience with failure, and Jim had wanted to make a good impression on the officer who had employed him "at his own value."

Ashley provided him with a fine horse and instructions as to the route the expedition had taken, and Jim set out. Riding as much as eight and ten hours a day, he soon overtook Captain Fitzpatrick, delivered the money and prepared to return to St. Louis. Before he started, however, an express came in saying that the general had decided to follow the party to the mountains and that he expected to overtake them when Fitzpatrick stopped to purchase horses.

The general was as good as his word, and the augmented band proceeded to Council Bluffs and then on into the Platte country. There they had the misfortune to lose all their recently purchased mounts in a surprise Indian raid. Since the party was afoot, it was impossible to follow the mounted Indians, so General Ashley returned to St. Louis, leaving Jim with Fitzpatrick's band to try to purchase more animals from friendlier tribes. This business required most of the summer and it was September when Jim returned to St. Louis to report on what Fitzpatrick had accomplished. He found Ashley again outfitting an expedition, determined to carry out his plans for making a fortune in the fur trade.

As hunter for the general's own band, Jim now set his face toward the distant, unseen Shining Mountains.

CHAPTER 5

Off to the Shining Mountains

XXXXXXXXXXXXXXXXXXXXXXXXXXXXXXXXXXXXXXXXXXXXXXXXXXXXX

The first few days passed without incident. Game was fairly plentiful and the men were not yet fatigued. As usual with such expeditions, the men were divided into groups of about ten. Each group ate and slept somewhat apart from the others, though close enough for safety. Each mess had its own cook and its own campfire around which the men sat and smoked and yarned before turning in for the night.

In Jim's mess was a young French boy, Baptiste La Jeunesse, from down New Orleans way. Baptiste knew little English, preferring French. Jim, with his natural skill at "catching on" to foreign languages, soon could understand this youth better than the other men did, or tried to do. Baptiste was lonely; he was grateful for Jim's understanding; and he admired Jim's skill and prowess. Jim, too, was lonely, and as he was younger than most of the engagés, or employes, it was natural that these two should become fast friends. Baptiste called Jim "mon frère," and Jim chose the youth as his hunting companion.

A week out of Fort Atkinson they caught up with Captain Fitzpatrick's group, and the augmented party moved on together. Three days later, Jim and Baptiste, who were out ahead looking for game, spied two horsemen, galloping toward them from the west. Unable to distinguish at first whether they were friends or foes, Jim called a warning to his companion. They drew rein and waited, guns ready.

The two men came on, whooping and waving tattered hats. Then Jim, too, gave a yell of recognition and spurred his horse forward.

"Black Harris!" he shouted. "So you're still above ground! I thought sure you'd been rubbed out, you old coyote!"

"Wagh! Ef it ain't Jim Beckwourth! Wal, this child sure 'nough thought ve wuz gone beaver!"

Jim turned to Black's companion and recognized another of Ashley's men.

"Old Dan Potts!" he exclaimed. "You, too! Then are the rest of the general's men still safe?" He was referring to a number of the party who had elected to stay on the prairie and not to return with General Ashley the preceding fall.

Potts grinned through his unkempt, grizzled beard. "Yep! Camped down hyar a few miles. Whar's the general, eh?"

Shouting the mountaineers' yell, "Wa-hoooo!" the quartet rode gaily back to Ashley's band. The general was genuinely glad to learn that this small group of men had survived the winter.

"But ye'd better hurry up, Gen'ral!" Black Harris observed, "er ye may find t'others starved to death. We ain't had much to eat fer a long time. Wagh!"

Jim shook his head in wonder. "It's a miracle that you ever found us!" he said to Harris.

The old mountaineer roared with amusement. "Ain't no miracle whatsomever! Jest keep to the buffler trails and yore bound to meet up with somebody!"

It was fortunate that Ashley arrived when he did, for the little band was nearly starved, as Black Harris had said. Worse even than the scarcity of food was the danger of a winter storm, which was now heralded by leaden skies and howling winds. Ashley's men hunched their shoulders and made what progress they could that afternoon.

The storm broke that night and raged for forty-eight hours without letup. The ground was covered with snow; game disappeared; but Ashley kept his hungry, freezing men on the move westward. Then, just when many were ready to lie down and await the end they felt was so close, a band of friendly Indians appeared. They were members of Two Axe's village, the same Pawnees who had rescued Jim the year before. They led the expedition to their village and Two Axe did his best to dissuade Ashley from trying to travel further during the winter.

Reports of the discussion filtered down through the ranks of the trappers. Old Dan Potts grumbled through his beard.

"Two Axe sez we kin stay here all winter—even offered me a good-lookin' squaw fer a wife. Gar! Why should we go batterin' our way acrost them mountings. It can't be done, nohow!"

Black Harris was more cheerful. "Ef the gen'ral sez it kin be done, we ain't got no choice, I reckon. Leastwise, I don't aim to make a choice. Where the gen'ral goes, Black goes. Wagh!"

Jim broke into the conversation. "I, for one, wouldn't mind spending the winter here. Plenty to eat; nice warm wigwams; games and sports. There's going to be a buffalo surround in a day or two. I could enjoy the winter here."

"Gen'ral's goin' to let us git in on that thar surround,"

Black Harris told Jim. "Ye'll see somethin' then that'll curl yore hair for sure."

"Why don't the general call a council and ask us all what we want to do?" Jim asked. "He talks to Fitzpatrick and Bill Sublette and Jim Clyman and a few of those he thinks so much of. But the rest of us——"

"He don't need our opinions," Black said shortly. "And I, fer one, wud druther he make the rules and I'll follow 'em."

That might be all right for Black, Jim thought gloomily, but he would like to know what was being planned. He didn't admit it to himself, but Jim was irked at the distinction General Ashley made among his men. In the officers' mess were several young men not much older than Jim. Of course, he conceded, Tom Fitzpatrick and Bill Sublette had been with the general for a couple of years now. They were not only experienced, they were smart and responsible. But Jim could not think that they were any better mountaineers than he was.

The day of the buffalo surround dawned bright and clear and cold. The Pawnee braves and the trappers rode out from the village to where high ridges rimmed a narrow canyon, leading from a wide valley where a herd of buffalo grazed. The swiftest riders of the Pawnees galloped down below the buffalo and then, with yells and screams and the waving of blankets, these young braves sent the buffaloes stampeding toward the canyon.

The great, shaggy beasts thundered over the frozen ground, heads down, stupidly unaware that they were heading straight into a trap. As they rushed into the canyon, Pawnees and trappers on the ridges shot them down by the hundreds.

Now the Pawnee squaws and children came up and began the work of butchering the slaughtered animals.

Great chunks of meat were hacked off and roasted over hastily made fires. There was feasting and singing and dancing, and Jim was in the very midst of it all. It was his first buffalo surround, but he took to it like a Pawnee, yelling the Indians' savage epithets as if he had been a veteran of these primitive tactics.

General Ashley did not join in the surround, but Jim saw with satisfaction that Captain Tom and Lieutenant Bill Sublette were not above having a bit of fun.

Ashley purchased some of the buffalo meat from Two Axe, as well as dried berries and some fresh horses, and then, in spite of the Pawnee chief's warning, the expedition set out again across the prairie.

It was bitter going, over drifted snow and icy streams, facing an arctic wind that howled down from the unseen mountains ahead. There was no game, and the newly purchased meat and berries were soon consumed. Now it was up to Jim as chief hunter to supply food for the cold and weary and hungry men. Jim ranged far and wide, riding when his famished horse could carry him, walking when the horse gave out. He covered more ground than anyone else, except faithful Baptiste who kept doggedly at his side. But it was useless work. The game had disappeared.

The other hunters had no better success, but as Jim came in to camp empty-handed night after night, the trappers looked at him with angry, desperate eyes. Even General Ashley, who suffered equally with his men, became irritable and unreasonable.

"Do you really try to find meat?" he asked Jim scornfully, "or do you get out of our sight and take a bit of a rest?"

Jim was about to make an insolent retort when Tom

Fitzpatrick interrupted. "Jim's the best hunter we have. If he doesn't bring in meat, there is no meat to be found."

Jim strode away to mutter his resentment to Baptiste.

Riding out alone one day because Baptiste was too weak to accompany him, Jim was betrayed into a violation of his responsibility as a hunter. He well knew the code—whatever game he found was to be brought in and divided according to the general's orders. But out there alone, far from camp, Jim came upon two teal ducks. He shot one, but the other rose and flew away. Jim gazed down at the lone victim of his rifle. It would not provide one mouthful apiece for the hungry men in camp. But for him alone, what a feast!

The temptation was too great. He quickly made a fire, roasted the duck and ate it. As his hunger was appeased his conscience took over, and he was ashamed of his act. He began to wonder how he could ever confess to those piercing, cold blue eyes of General Ashley. Everlasting contempt would certainly be his reward.

The only thing to do now was to find sufficient game to give the trappers a good meal. Luck favored him, and he soon brought down a large elk. He hurried back to camp to send out a couple of men to bring in the meat. As he went, he planned exactly how he would explain that he had had to eat the duck in order to have strength enough to carry on until he discovered the elk.

He never uttered the explanation. It was more than he could bring himself to do.

The men were jubilant. Where they had heaped blame upon him when he was unsuccessful, now they showered him with praise. Jim was a hero. The men laughed and chattered and gobbled great chunks of roasted meat. Jim wasn't hungry. As he ate sparingly of the elk, not

daring to refuse it altogether, he saw General Ashley's
eye upon him. He began to wonder whether the officer
suspected what he had done.

Perhaps it was Jim's imagination, fired by his regret-
ful conscience, that made him think that from that day
Ashley was more curt and disdainful in his attitude toward the hunter. And perhaps it was just that all their
nerves were growing frayed and sore from the intermi-
nable cold and hunger and the heartbreaking effort of
battling the wind and the snow. But whatever the
reason, Jim began to feel that Ashley despised him, and
the joy of the adventure was gone.

The men plodded on, day after desperate day. On
Christmas they "lay over" and Ashley handed out a
ration of rum and sugar to each man. They accepted
the gift gratefully and tried to make a small celebration,
but they had little heart for it. The New Year came in,
and the bitter weeks of January wheeled slowly past,
and they had not yet reached the Shining Mountains.

Then one clear, cold February day Jim was riding
ahead as usual, so as to reach any possible game before
it was frightened away by the advancing column. Peering ahead, his eyes caught something on the horizon. He
shaded them with his hands and stared. There, sure
enough, far ahead rose a shining, snow-capped peak.
The slanting rays of the morning sun touched it with
glittering rose. Jim sat still, his dark eyes filled with wonder. The Shining Mountains!

Then boisterous joy filled him. He wheeled his horse
and galloped back to the column, yelling, "The Shining
Mountains! Wa-hooo!"

The others hurried ahead, straining their eyes to catch
the dazzling, inspiring sight.

"Yes!" Tom Fitzpatrick agreed, "that's Long's Peak—

first thing we see of the Rockies—or Stonies—or as Jim calls them, the Shining Mountains. And well-named they are, no matter which name we use. That peak is the one General Stephen Long first saw when he was out this way five years ago."

The new men yelled and danced with joy, thinking their journey nearly over, but the seasoned trappers warned them, "There's a mighty long way yet to go."

With renewed courage, the hungry, weary men moved on. Two weeks later they were at the foot of a high range of buttes which Ashley was sure no white man had ever tried to cross. It required three days of the most difficult labor to get men, horses, wagons and supplies up over this range. But once over, the land opened out into wide, pleasant valleys and they made their way swiftly to the banks of a broad river.

"Well, sir!" Fitzpatrick announced genially, "here we are on the banks of the Green River, or the Siskadee as the Indians call it. The trappers gave it the first name because its waters reflect the green willows along the banks. The Indians named it for the abundance of prairie chickens to be found among those willows."

General Ashley beamed. "We made it over the mountains in midwinter," he declared exultantly. "We made it with loaded wagons—the first ever to cross the mountains. And without the loss of a man! This deserves a celebration."

Celebrate they did, feasting on prairie chicken and buffalo, while their famished horses reveled in the lush grass and sweet willows.

Here General Ashley decided to divide his men into small bands to trap along the neighboring streams until time for the summer rendezvous, or gathering in of trappers and Indians.

"I have a hankering to explore this stream," he said. "I believe I can carry my supplies downstream more easily and cheaply than I can move them over the rest of the way in wagons. So set to work, men. Build me some stout bullboats!"

The seasoned trappers knew just what to do and the newcomers learned fast. The boat frames of stout willows were speedily lashed together. Over these frames were stretched buffalo hides. The bowl-shaped boats were light and buoyant and were much used by trappers along the western rivers. When the boats were ready, Ashley called his entire company together and explained what he wanted done.

"I am going to go down this river about a hundred miles, or until I find a suitable place for our summer rendezvous. The site I select will be plainly marked so it can easily be found. I'll also send out word by any trappers or Indians I meet. I want you all to be in that place early in July—by the tenth at the latest."

Jim was listening eagerly, his hope bright that he might be chosen to go on this exciting river trip with the general.

"I'm going to take six men with me, with Mr. Sublette as my lieutenant. The rest of you I'll break up into small parties and send you out in different directions to trap until July."

Baptiste tugged at Jim's buckskin shirt sleeve.

"Mon frère," he said urgently, "when you are named partisan, you will not forget me, eh?"

"Partisan! You think——"

"But of course! Who else so well deserves honor? And Mr. Fitzpatrick, he say Beckwourth should be partisan."

Jim's heart leaped. Perhaps the boy was right. Perhaps Ashley would name him partisan, or captain, of one of the outgoing squads. And why not? He had worked hard all winter; he had brought in food when no other hunter was successful. He had proved his skill and his fortitude. To be named partisan on his first trip out to the mountains would be a tribute to cherish. Earned, yes, but therefore all the more desirable.

"Mr. Fitzpatrick," Ashley was saying in his clipped, decisive voice, "select six men and travel southwest, toward those mountains." He nodded toward distant peaks. "William Ham, you take six and go south toward the Tewinty Mountains. And Clyman, you take Joseph LaBarge, Jim Beckwourth, Baptiste La Jeunesse, Dan Potts and a couple of others and go north along this river, trapping its tributaries."

Jim turned slowly away from the chattering groups of men. He had not been named a partisan. He had not even been left free to be chosen by Fitzpatrick, but had been assigned to Clyman's brigade—assigned, as if no one would choose him freely. Well, there was one thing —Baptiste would be with him.

More disappointed than he would admit, even to himself, Jim gathered together his paraphernalia and waited for the stern Clyman to lead out.

CHAPTER 6

Jim Becomes a Mountain Man

XXXXXXXXXXXXXXXXXXXXXXXXXXXXXXXXXXXXXXXXXXXXXXXXXXXXX

James Clyman, partisan of the small brigade to which Jim was attached, was a rather dour Scotsman, who had little respect for the average fellow employed by General Ashley. Clyman had been in the general's employ for nearly three years now, having gone to the mountains with the second segment of the 1822 expedition.

As the little group moved northward toward the sources of the Green, Clyman unhesitatingly assumed the leadership, and let it be understood that he would stand for no nonsense among his men. Jim's vague and formless hope, that Clyman would prove inept as captain, died, and he had to content himself with taking orders from the curt Scotsman.

But at the campfire, Jim regained some of his glory. Here, far from General Ashley's stern eye, he could indulge in all sorts of fantastic make-believe, and his yarns held his listeners spellbound. Even his differences with Ashley in the months just past, differences in which the general had undoubtedly come off the victor, were now elaborated and embroidered into great tales of derring-do in which Jim boldly and unflinchingly stood up to the general, or saved his life, or bested him in some test of skill or prowess.

Clyman listened silently and dourly to these extravagant yarns, but the men swallowed them avidly. Even when they knew for a certainty that the facts differed widely from the telling, they didn't care. Jim, as he pictured himself, did the things each one of them would have liked to do, even though none of them had the imagination even to dream of acting in such roles.

Sometimes, as if to counteract Jim's exuberant tales, the silent Clyman relaxed and told a story of his own. And he had stories to tell. He had been with Captain Jed Smith when that intrepid leader fought a huge white grizzly bear and had had one side of his face torn off in the encounter. Clyman had been the one who sewed up the wounds as best he could. He had known Hugh Glass, who had been left for dead after an encounter with a grizzly and had crawled and stumbled a hundred miles to an Indian camp, intent on finding and punishing those who had deserted him. Clyman could tell of life in a Crow camp where he had spent one winter with Jed Smith's party; with the captain reading his Bible every night while his hands fondled the deep fur of his pet beaver.

Clyman had plenty of stories to tell, and he told them with a cool detachment, a paucity of phrase, that made them terribly real to his listeners. But they liked Jim's stories best, embroidered as they were with yelling Indians, bloody scalping knives, and feats of prodigious strength and endurance. These yarns transported them beyond the confines of their isolated camp, beyond the banks of the Green River; and each of Jim's listeners became, for the time, a hero, too.

Trapping was excellent here on the upper reaches of the Green. Almost every trap raised held a beaver. On Horse Creek, where the Crows had stolen some of Jed Smith's horses, the brigade took more than a hundred

beaver in a week. The skins were worth $10 a pound in
St. Louis; sixty skins forming a pack of 100 pounds.

One day when the brigade was working along a small
creek, a band of Indians came into camp. Jim had his
hand upon his gun, when the Indians began to shout,
"Bueno! Bueno!"

"Don't shoot!" Clyman ordered. "They are friendly.
They speak Spanish!"

There were sixteen Indians in the party, and Clyman
welcomed them into camp, where they sat about jabbering in a dialect none of the brigade could understand.
As the hours passed the Indians grew more and more
garrulous, more and more confident. They began to
handle articles that belonged to the trappers. When they
reached for Jim's gun it was too much.

"They're too friendly!" he expostulated with Clyman.
"It's just Indian nature to take advantage of us if we
give them half a chance."

Clyman and the others, however, jeered at Jim's caution. Then one of the Indians picked up some stacked
guns and started to run away with them. Jim and Baptiste set out after him, recovered the weapons and
brought them back.

"You'll make them mad," Clyman said angrily, "and
we can't afford to anger them, alone here as we are."

"They wuz jest jokin'," grumbled Joe La Barge. "That's
jest the Injun way of playin'."

Jim shook his head. "I've been among the Indians—not
these, but others—and they're all much alike. I don't
trust that kind of joke. Let's move out onto the open
prairie where we can at least see them, if they come upon
us. With these trees and bushes all around, we're gone
beaver if they take a notion for a scalping party."

Jim's idea was voted down, and that night, so confident were they all, that only one man was set to guard the camp. This was Joe La Barge, who had one of the friendly Indians to keep him company at the campfire. The other trappers rolled in their blankets and slept.

A shrill shriek of anguish awakened the camp and sent every hand reaching for the gun that lay close within the blanket of each man. As Jim's fingers closed on the stock of his rifle, they encountered other fingers, there before his. A young Indian was just snatching the rifle. Jim, wide-awake immediately, wrested the gun from the red man's hand, and started flailing with it, trying to hit the shadowy form as it dodged out of reach.

Jim ran toward the fire. There, stretched out on the ground was La Barge, a tomahawk buried in his skull. Jim stooped and pulled the weapon from its gruesome bed, and a stream of blood spurted over his hand. He knelt to examine the wound and found it deep enough to bury his four fingers in it.

Jim shook his head sadly over his dead companion, but there was no time to be wasted. He leaped to his feet, peering into the darkness. Not an Indian could be seen. They were hiding, he felt sure, among the trees that ringed the camp.

Clyman said, anguish in his voice, "We must get out of here. Get your things together——"

Jim's moccasined foot scattered the glowing coals of the fire, which offered a clear target to the unseen enemy. In the complete darkness, the men fumbled for their belongings, threw their packs together, and were ready to slip, single file and in silence, down along the creek bank to more open ground.

There was little heart left for trapping in this region, and Clyman suggested that they make their way to the rendezvous, even though it was far too early for the as-

signed meeting. The others were glad to get away from
the unhappy spot, so they started out southward.

The next day they met up with a party of sixteen of
Ashley's men, captained by one Castenga, a man Jim
had known in St. Louis. They had been in the mountains for two years, had lost a few men through Indian
attacks, but had successfully trapped many streams and
were in possession of rich packs of beaver for the general. They did not know, however, that Ashley had come
to the mountains.

The two parties spent the night rejoicing and gossip-
ing. In the morning, re-enforced by several of these
doughty fellows, Jim went back to bury the body of the
slain La Barge. They could find nothing, however, excepting a shank of long black hair, matted with blood.
Unhappily they returned to the others, deciding to call
the creek La Barge in honor of their comrade.

The enlarged party now moved on down the river,
and without trouble found the place marked by Ashley
for the rendezvous. It was still early and they were the
first party to come in, but that did not discomfit them
any. They had plenty of beaver to allay any impatience
the general might show toward their early arrival. And
there was enough activity to keep them amused—horse
racing, wrestling, storytelling and eating to fill the summer hours.

Gradually small parties began to arrive, for the word
had been sent out through all the mountains that there
was to be a grand rendezvous this summer. There were
groups of Ashley men; free trappers alone or in twos and
threes; Indians of all tribes from the Canadian border to
Santa Fe.

By July first a great and motley throng had assembled.
All of Ashley's men were now present: Jedediah Smith's

Salt Lake band among them, with a rich store of peltries they had purchased for a song from trappers of the rival Hudson's Bay Company. Jim looked curiously at this young captain, who seemed to hold a place of unique prestige among all who knew him. He saw a tall, serious-faced young man, whose long, soft brown hair was carefully combed down over the right side of his face to hide the ear Jim Clyman had sewed on crookedly when it had been torn off by the grizzly bear. One eyebrow, not perfectly joined, gave a quizzical look to the intent young face.

Jim noticed that General Ashley greeted Jed Smith with more warmth than he had shown toward any other employee, and they conversed together long and quietly beside the campfire. The other trappers in from the mountains welcomed Jim Clyman and Black Harris with shouts of welcome and boisterous jeers. "Gar, we shore thought you wuz rubbed out!" or "How come yore here? Heard ye was gone beaver!" and other jolly comments upon the survival of those who had been absent for some time.

Black Harris, happening to pass by Jim, hunkered down for a sociable chat.

"Gar! Did ye ever see sech a bunch of men? Prime beaver, every one of 'em. Ashley's got the cream of the crop, ef it does sound like braggin'!"

Jim nodded. They were Mountain Men all right, and he hoped to be counted among them. He must know them all.

"Who's that fellow over there?" he asked Black. "Don't look any older than Baptiste, here."

"That's Jim Bridger—Old Gabe he's called in the mountings. He's an old hand, he is. Came out when he was a younker of seventeen. An' there's Old Frapp, and

Caleb Greenwood—nobuddy knows how long old Caleb's been in the mountings. And that fellow with the torn shirt—that's Johnson Gardner. He's a joker, wagh! Ye know whut he done? Made a flag out of his old red flannel shirt and his winter underpants, he did. The Hudson's Bay men had run up a British flag over their cabin out on the shores of the Great Salt Lake. Johnson took his fancy flag over and made 'em haul down the Union Jack and raise up Old Glory. It wuz somethin' to see, I betcha. The whole brigade's been braggin' about it."

Jim listened eagerly, and as Black talked he imagined himself an old-timer, the subject of wild tales and fanciful yarns. But there were others he must know about: Etienne Provost, whose experiences on the Santa Fe trail had already made him a figure of romance; Davy Jackson, another of Ashley's men of 1822; Doc Newell, Robert Campbell—Jim felt his head reeling with all the adventures these men had known.

"An' now yore in the mountings," Black said finally, "ye mought as well git used to the mounting names. Out here we use Injun handles——"

Jim nodded, "Like they call you Black, instead of Moses?"

"Wal, my name's stuck on so well I can't shake it, nohow. Even down in St. Louie I'm Black Harris. But the others, most of 'em drop their Injun name when they git to civilization. Now Tom, you know what he's called?"

"Of course. Clyman told me the Indians call him Broken Hand ever since he accidentally shot off three fingers."

"That's correct. An' Jim Bridger's called Old Gabe, because he gabs so much. He's almost as big a liar as I be. Wagh!"

Jim made a mental note of this. He would have to get

down to business around the rendezvous campfires if he wanted to maintain his reputation as a gaudy liar. With Black and that Old Gabe on hand, it would be a contest worth hearing!

"Bill Sublette, now," Black went on, "he's Cut Face on account of that scar across his cheek. Ye'll be given a Injun name, too, I reckon."

"I have already," Jim said quietly. "Up on the Green —those Indians that came into camp took a fancy to my knife." He drew from his belt the elegant hunting knife he had purchased with some of his money from the lead mines. Unlike the ordinary trapper's knife with its dark horn or wood haft, Jim's knife had a handle of gleaming white ivory. It was his proudest possession next to his favorite horse, Golden Arrow. Now he balanced it on his palm and said, "They called me White-Handled Knife. Guess that will do for a moniker!"

When everyone had come in, General Ashley broke out his merchandise and the trading began. Packs of furs—beaver, muskrat, otter, buffalo hides and deerskins —were tossed into piles while William Sublette and the general measured out the pay in new traps, ammunition, sugar, coffee, tobacco for the white trappers; or bright red cloth, glass beads, and brassbound penny mirrors for the Indians.

As soon as a man had turned in his pelts and received his pay, he joined the merrymakers at the edge of the clearing. Here fist fights with eye-gouging, nose-biting, and belly-stomping were boisterously encouraged and lavishly bet on. Horse races, wrestling matches, contests of strength, gambling, drinking, singing all went on with great noise and jollity.

It was a brash, roistering party, the one wholly uninhibited gathering of the trappers' year. But so strictly

did Ashley and his lieutenant attend to business that by
the afternoon of the second day the general had con-
cluded his trading and was ready to pack up his peltries
and set out for home. He was wildly enthusiastic over
the results of this year's work. He had suffered many re-
verses during the past three years, but now, heaped up
around him were enough furs to wipe out all his debts
and leave him a comfortable fortune, besides.

Jim's special talents as wrestler, fighter, horse racer,
storyteller made him a great favorite at the rendezvous,
and he was enjoying himself immensely. He wouldn't
have minded staying on after the general departed, but
was content to leave when Ashley named him as one of
the twenty men whom he had chosen to accompany him
and his fortune in furs back to St. Louis. He was particularly proud of this distinction when he found that
others so honored included the matchless Jed Smith and
the indomitable Jim Bridger.

Ashley's plan was to take the furs by horse pack to the
Big Horn. There they would be placed in bullboats and
floated down the Yellowstone and Missouri to Fort Atkinson, where they would be transferred to steamboats for
the last leg of the long journey to the fur capital of the
world.

The trip to the river was made without much trouble,
excepting one small encounter with Crows, to whom
General Ashley made presents, cementing a strong
friendship this tribe had always shown for the whites.

At the river, the men set to work building the necessary bullboats. Manning each with a couple of trappers
and loading them with furs, the brigade started downstream. They had progressed some 800 miles when they
came near the site of Andrew Henry's ill-fated fort.
Henry had been Ashley's partner, but the disasters that

seemed to dog his footsteps in every undertaking had soured him on the fur business and he had withdrawn. Ashley wanted to look over this site of special interest to him, so decided to camp here for a day or two.

As the men were pulling into the shore, one of the bullboats capsized, sending the general's valuable furs bobbing downstream.

Ashley, on shore, let out a yell. "To the river, men! Rescue those peltries!"

The men who could swim leaped into the river; the others stood on shore, yelling and shouting. Suddenly a band of soldiers appeared, out of nowhere, it seemed, demanding an explanation of the ruckus. When they saw what was happening, they joined in the general confusion by shouting instructions to the swimmers. No one had time to notice the newcomers until after the dripping men had dragged the sodden bundles ashore. There they spread the furs to dry, so they would not be damaged by their soaking.

Then Ashley turned to a young officer and asked, "Where do you come from?"

The officer explained. He was Lieutenant Stephen Watts Kearny with General Atkinson's forces, who had just been upriver on a visit to the Crow nation. He invited Ashley's whole party to the army camp, where they rested for several days, enjoying the hospitality, food and yarns of the soldiers.

But the pleasant interlude had to end, and at last Ashley's men were moving downriver again. At Fort Clark they ran into another of the general's old friends, Joshua Pilcher, who insisted on presenting Ashley with a grizzly bear for a pet. This pet soon became more of a nuisance than anything else, and General Ashley handed its care over to Jim.

At Council Bluffs the peltries were transferred to a steamboat, and the journey was nearly over.

General Ashley, well aware of the value of letting the public know what he was doing, stopped at St. Charles in order to send an express ahead to announce his coming. As a result, a huge throng was at the dock when the boat reached St. Louis.

Jim anxiously scanned the massed crowd below him, hoping to see a familiar face. He recognized no one and, sadly disappointed, turned his attention to the bear. General Ashley had ordered him to take the animal to the officer's home. The bear, which had become a rather obstreperous customer, was restrained on a long chain, but Jim was the only one with the strength and the stubbornness to control the huge animal.

As they left the boat, the crowd dropped back, horrified at the sight of the shaggy beast. Jim was struggling up the steep cobbled street, tugging at the bear's chain to keep him in tow, when he heard his name called. He turned and there, running toward him, was his father. Jim almost let go of the bear's leash as he reached out to grasp his father in an affectionate hug.

"Jim! How are you? I've been so afraid you might have been killed!"

Jim chuckled. "Not me, Father. I always manage to escape, somehow. But how are you?" He studied his father with shocked, loving eyes. In the past year his hair had become white, his military figure stooped and trembling.

"I've been ill, Jim. But the sight of you makes me well again."

"Tom?" Jim asked quickly. "Does he take good care of you?"

"Tom's sold the place and gone East—to Washington. He wants to get into the political life there——"

Many questions were crowding Jim's tongue, but the bear was pulling and tugging and must be attended to first.

"Let me get this critter up to the general's house," he said. "Then we'll go someplace and have dinner and you can tell me about everything: Madame Beckwourth, Matilda, Louise—yourself most of all."

Eating with his father that night, watching the man's trembling hands, hearing his faltering voice, Jim was filled with remorse that he had been away when his father needed him. He should never have trusted Tom, he told himself bitterly. Mrs. Beckwourth had died; Tom had moved away.

"I did what I promised you, Jim. I gave Matilda and Louise their freedom. They are both married now and live here in St. Louis, but I don't see them often. I have a room in a boardinghouse——"

"Money?" Jim asked. "Do you have plenty of money?"

The major shrugged. "I lost a lot one way and another. And when Tom sold the place, he needed the money to get started on his career. But I manage."

"I'll get my pay tomorrow, and then we'll fix you up," Jim promised.

General Ashley proved to be a generous paymaster and Jim had plenty of money to show his father a good time and buy him some new clothes. And he had time to give him what he needed most, loving companionship. Jim was proud and happy to be able to repay in some measure all that his father had done for him in the past. He was somewhat exultant, too, that it was he, and not Tom, who was making the old man happy.

Jim visited Matilda and Louise, sought out a few of his old cronies, and savored to the full the life of the bustling fur metropolis. But he enjoyed this freedom for only three days. On the fourth General Ashley sent for him.

"I want you to return to the mountains, Beckwourth," he said.

"Yes, sir. I'll be ready. When does your next company leave, sir?"

"I want you to start tomorrow."

"Tomorrow!" Jim gasped. "Why, sir, I just got home."

"I know that as well as you do," Ashley said curtly, "but I have some dispatches that must go immediately to Captain Sublette. La Roche and Pellow can go with you. How about it?"

Jim shrugged. "If you wish it, sir," was all he said.

The next morning Jim and his two companions again faced westward. Each had two saddle horses, and there was one mule to carry bedding and supplies. Inside Jim's buckskin shirt reposed the dispatches for Bill Sublette.

As the fresh horses stepped out at a brisk canter, Jim looked back at the city.

"I feel like a sailor," he muttered, "just in port after a year at sea—and ordered to leave on the next ship." Then he shrugged. "But I am the one the general chose. I am the one he trusts when he has an important job to be done."

His shoulders straightened, his chin lifted, and he began to sing: "Hooray, hooray for the mountains!"

CHAPTER 7

The Trapper's Life

xxxxxxxxxxxxxxxxxxxxxxxxxxxxxxxxxxxxxxxxxxxxxxxxxxxxx

The journey to the mountains was made without untoward incident. Jim and his two companions, both seasoned mountain men, traveled swiftly and safely over the route they had come to know so well. Jim knew that a winter rendezvous had been set for Willow Valley, some seventy-five miles north of the Great Salt Lake, so instead of trying to find Bill Sublette somewhere in the vast western region, he headed straight for the valley to await Bill's coming in. He reached his destination late in October.

There Jim found some of Ashley's men already encamped, while Indians, free trappers, and small brigades of Ashley's men kept coming in from day to day until there was quite a gathering there in the sheltered valley. Bill Sublette's brigade, however, was the very last one to arrive. Jim delivered his dispatches, and then, the season being so late, decided he would not try to return to St. Louis that year, but would remain with the trappers in the mountains.

The dispatches proved to be imperative orders for Bill Sublette to come at once to St. Louis. Jedediah Smith was negotiating a partnership with General Ashley, who wanted his right-hand man there to assist and approve the project. Sublette ordered that the pelts already taken be cached here in Willow Valley and the winter camp then be moved southward some fifty miles to Ogden's Hole, near the junction of the Ogden and Weber rivers. Then, with only Black Harris as his companion, Bill set out for St. Louis, leaving Tom Fitzpatrick in charge of all of Ashley's men and operations.

This winter camp was somewhat of a departure from the usual practice. It had been the custom for trappers, either singly or in small brigades, to spend the winter in an established post or some friendly Indian village. There, often, a trapper would take an Indian wife, who would follow him when summer came to the rendezvous and up and down the streams of the West as he carried on his work of obtaining peltries.

The children of such a couple took the hard, unsheltered life as a matter of course. They were wild little things, "strong and healthy as bears," Jim described them. And though many died from illness or were killed or stolen by raiding Indians, others grew to maturity and were sometimes sent to St. Louis to school. Old Caleb Greenwood, one of the oldest mountain men in the encampment, had his son with him—a young man who had known nothing but the wild, free life of a trapper.

Life in the winter camp was very pleasant and easy. There was plenty of elk and antelope for food, good trapping for occupation, and dances, revelry and Indian fights for recreation. Jim was introduced to one aspect of this last form of excitement when a band of Bannocks swept down from the north and drove off eighty horses belonging to the trappers.

Tom Fitzpatrick couldn't let such an insult go unanswered. With some forty men, Jim among them, he set out to recapture the animals. As they neared the Bannock camp, Tom divided his party into two groups, one under his command, and the other under young Jim

Bridger. Beckwourth was in the second party. While
Fitzpatrick's band made a feint at assaulting the village,
thus keeping the attention of the Bannock braves,
Bridger's group raided the horses and drove off not only
their own animals, but about fifty of the Bannocks'.

When the victorious party returned to camp, they
found the winter village augmented by some eight hundred Snakes. These Indians were friendly, this was their
old hunting ground, and so they were welcomed and
treated well by the trappers. During the winter these
Snakes joined the trappers in retaliatory raids against
the ever-hostile and annoying Bannocks.

All winter long there was talk about the great Salt
Lake that lay to the westward. In the previous fall, while
the trappers were encamped in Willow Valley, Jim
Bridger had floated in a bullboat down the Bear River
to this mysterious body of water, and he never let pass
an opportunity to tell of his adventure.

"Lor!" he would say chuckling, "I dipped my hands in
an' scooped up some o' that pretty blue water an' started
to take a drink. But Lor! I sure spit it out mighty darned
quick! It wuz that salty! I thought sure it wuz the Pacific
Ocean, I did!"

The trappers were eager to learn more about this fearsome body of water, concerning which both white man
and red had many a superstitious tale. Toward spring,
Jim Clyman could wait no longer.

"You fellows build me a bullboat and I'll go clean
around the lake and see what there is to see."

The bullboat was immediately constructed and Clyman, with Louis Vasquez, Henry Fraeb, and Daniel
Potts set out amid the cheers and jokes of the trappers.
The "seafaring brigade" did not return to Camp until
well into the summer, and they had little to report.

"It's about four hundred miles around," Clyman informed the eager trappers. "The shore barren. The water so salty it won't dissolve any more that's thrown into it."

"The River Buenaventura we've heard so much about," Fitzpatrick asked. "Did you find it?"

"Nary a sign of it, sir. Only found two rivers. One's the outlet to the Utah Lake. 'Tother's Weber's River, where we've camped."

Before sending his brigades out in the spring, Fitzpatrick cached the furs already trapped or brought in by Indians. Then they made ready to disperse for the summer.

Jim had a choice to make. He could go out as a free trapper, or skin trapper, at liberty to go wherever he pleased and to sell his pelts to whomever he chose, giving Ashley, of course, the first chance to bid on them. Or he could go out as an Ashley man, equipped and supplied by the company, with the stipulation that he would be paid for each pelt he brought in. Or, if he wished, he could be employed by the company at a definite wage, and this would be all he would get, no matter how many or how few beaver he trapped. Jim decided on the second course, and signed up for a year.

He was assigned to the brigade led by Broken Hand, who had determined to venture into the territory of the treacherous Blackfeet. The small company advanced cautiously, finding the trapping excellent, as few had dared to undertake such a dangerous project. They had several encounters with raiding Blackfeet, but managed to hold their own. On the Sage River they came upon Jim's old companion, Black Harris, with another old-timer, Portuleuse. These two were the advance scouts for General Ashley, who, with Bill Sublette, Jedediah Smith and a large caravan, was on his way from St. Louis with supplies for the summer rendezvous. They exchanged news and gossip, and then the scouts rode on, while Tom's brigade proceeded with its trapping.

A few days later a small band of Flatheads caught up with the brigade. Through their interpreter they told Tom that there was a party of white men, with women and children, stranded some fifteen miles away. They had guns, the Indians said, but no ammunition, and they were in a precarious position, as a party of hostile Indians was dogging their trail.

Fitzpatrick, always energetic, lost no time in meeting this situation. "That must be Robert Campbell's party," he said. "Who will carry ammunition to him and his people?"

Jim stepped forward, as did several others. Fitzpatrick's blue Irish eyes scanned the volunteers and selected three. "Beckwourth, Provost, Gervais! You'll do!"

The trio took a supply of ammunition from the brigade store and set out. Jim, who was riding his beautiful Golden Arrow, found it easy to keep the lead as they followed the direction indicated by the friendly Indians. Before long he sighted the party they had come to assist.

"Campbell!" Jim shouted. "We thought it must be your party. We have brought you ammunition."

"We are certainly glad, Jim! Your party must be close?"

"About fifteen miles ahead, and going slow so you can catch up with them. Have you had any trouble?"

"Not yet," Campbell answered, "but there are Indians all around us. So far we've not lost a man, and we're bringing in some fine beaver packs for the general."

The party now moved on more confidently, eager to catch up with Fitzpatrick. They traveled until late that night, made camp and posted guard. The night passed quietly, and it was with untroubled minds that they started out next morning.

Suddenly Jim heard singing behind him. Turning his head, he was astonished to see a large band of Indians riding toward him.

"Flatheads! Flatheads!" shouted some of the trappers.

Jim, Etienne Provost and Baptiste Gervais, having the fastest horses, rode back to meet their supposed friends. When they came nearer to the galloping Indians they saw with shock that these were not Flatheads, but hostile Blackfeet.

The three trappers didn't wait for introductions. Whirling their horses, they galloped back to Campbell's party.

"Put the women and children on the fastest horses," Jim ordered. "Send them flying to that clump of willows—"

"It's six miles away, at least!" Campbell cried.

"It's our only hope. We can hold off the Indians while the women and children escape."

There was no time to argue. The women leaped onto the horses, taking the children up behind them, and away they galloped toward the distant clump of willows. The trappers, mounting the slower horses, or on foot, turned to face the oncoming foe. They were in a fairly good position, with a small lake on one side of them and a steep hill on the other. The Blackfeet could not flank them; instead they came head on, showering the trappers with a hail of arrows.

The trappers, cool and ready, waited until the Indians were close and then fired. They had the satisfaction of hearing screams of pain and seeing several of the braves fall to the ground.

Slowly the trappers backed toward the willows, repelling again and again the vicious charges of the Blackfeet. The trappers had an advantage with their guns and their sure aim. The Indians, letting fly their arrows while their horses were at full gallop, could not aim accurately and many of the deadly missiles went wild.

Keeping one eye on the fleeing women, Jim saw that they had gained the willows, and he gave a sigh of relief. It was cut short by a shrill scream of pain.

"Help! Help! I'm wounded!"

Jim saw with horror that old Bolliere was bent over his horse's neck with an arrow sticking out of his back.

"Help!" Jim shouted, "we must save him!" and he galloped toward the old trapper. Gervais spurred his horse to ride with Jim into the storm of arrows. They caught up with the old trapper and Jim jerked the arrow from his back. He slapped the horse on the flank and wheeled his own Golden Arrow for the dash back to safety. But Bolliere couldn't make it; he slid to the ground with a groan.

The Blackfeet were upon Jim and Gervais. It looked as if they could not escape. But the trappers' mounts were the best to be had. Leaping a slough they put distance between them and their pursuers, and were soon back in the comparative safety of the willows.

The howling Blackfeet circled the sheltering clump, yelling and shrieking. Before long, Jim feared, they would fire the willows, and that would be the end. Someone must make a dash for help.

One of the trappers, Eroquey, put Jim's thought into words, and sixteen of the men leaped eagerly to horse, ready to dash through the encircling Blackfeet and attempt to reach Fitzpatrick. They were driven back. Jim's horse was shot from under him, and he was left afoot among the howling savages.

Back in camp, young Baptiste saw his friend's plight. Leaping upon his horse he galloped out and took Jim up behind him and back to safety, while arrows rained around them. Jim was wounded slightly when an arrow struck his forehead, but he scarcely knew it in the haste and danger of the moment.

Finding that so large a party could not break through the enemies' lines, Jim and a trapper named Calhoun decided to try it. Stripping to a breechcloth, tying their long hair with a bright strip of cloth, they thought they might pass through without attracting attention.

The ruse worked for a few moments, and the two daring emissaries had a good start before the Blackfeet realized what had happened. With a yell they were in pursuit. But Jim and Calhoun, bent low over the fleetest horses Campbell's men could offer, rushed on, and soon outdistanced their pursuers.

They had not far to go. There, ahead of them, came a small band of trappers.

"Where's the fight?" they called. "We heard the shooting——"

"Ahead! Ahead!" Jim shouted. "Someone ride back for help and I'll lead you to the besieged band!"

He wheeled his horse and started back with the mountaineers behind him shouting their famous "Wah-hoo-hoo!"

When the Blackfeet saw re-enforcements coming they did not wait to discover how many were in the band. They scattered into the hills. Jim rode over and picked up Bolliere's body and carried it into the willows for burial.

The fight had lasted five desperate hours. Four of the trappers had been killed and seven wounded, but not a woman or child had been injured. It was impossible to tell how many of the Blackfeet had been slain. The trappers had seventeen scalps as trophies, but many of the bodies had been carried away by the decamping Indians.

The trappers hastened on to join Fitzpatrick; then all together they went on to the rendezvous at Willow Valley.

"Better call it Cache Valley now," Jim suggested grinning. "We have the biggest cache of peltries waiting for General Ashley that he's ever seen."

Fitzpatrick's blue eyes twinkled. "Cache Valley it is, Jim, and a better name than Willow—there are many valleys filled with willows, but only one in which Ashley's furs are hidden."

They had barely reached the valley when General Ashley came in with a huge caravan of goods. With him were Jed Smith and Bill Sublette and many of Jim's old friends and companions. From all parts of the West came trappers and Indians to enjoy the rendezvous.

Before things could get under way, however, the old Snake chieftain O-Mo-gua came into camp. He sought out Bill Sublette and told him that two Snake women had been killed by the Blackfeet.

"You say your men are brave, Cut Face," he said, using the name the Indians gave Sublette because of a scar across his face. "Now let me see them fight, that I may know your words are true."

Thus appealed to, Bill called upon his trappers and a great band set out to avenge the wrong done their friends, the Snakes. Jim, of course, could not be left behind, and rode out in the foremost rank. They soon met up with the enemy and had a fierce engagement that lasted some six hours, before the Blackfeet were driven to seek refuge in flight. The triumphant trappers rode gaily back to camp, flaunting a hundred scalps from their lances.

The victory was celebrated with a great scalp dance and feast. When the rejoicing was at its height, General Ashley called his men together and made a speech.

He was leaving the mountains, he said, a rich man, due to the loyalty and energy of the trappers. He had sold his entire interest in the fur trade, including the contracts of the men in his employ, to Jed Smith, David Jackson and Bill Sublette.

"Whenever any of you come to St. Louis," he said, "your first duty must be to call at my house to talk over the scenes of peril we have encountered together. Farewell, mountaineers and friends! May God bless you all!"

Cheers filled the air. The men were sorry to see the general depart. He had been a friend to all and had given them a new and exciting festival—the summer rendezvous.

Before he left, General Ashley found a chance to say farewell privately to Jim. "While I've been here I have heard many stories of your exploits, Beckwourth," he said. "Mr. Fitzpatrick says you have proved to be brave, reliable and loyal. I like brave men, but some of these stories lead me to think that you are reckless as well as brave—that you will undertake any exploit if you think it will impress your companions. Correct this fault, Beckwourth, take care of yourself, and you will live to a ripe old age. And whenever you come to St. Louis, be sure to visit me."

Jim could find no words to answer the general's kind

advice. He had at times been resentful of the officer's stern authority over him, but now Jim was remembering only the kindnesses, the little acts of generosity. Emotional as he was, he felt his throat grow tight as he silently shook Ashley's hand in parting.

CHAPTER 8

A Joke Backfires

‹‹

As soon as General Ashley had left for St. Louis with his one hundred and twenty-three packs of beaver, the three new owners set to work getting the new firm into operation. The young men divided their duties. Jedediah Smith with a party of fifteen set out to explore the region south and west of the Great Salt Lake. Davy Jackson, the quiet, unobtrusive member of the firm, took a brigade of trappers northward. William Sublette was to handle the business end of the firm. He would keep to a central position with his band of trappers, and when the peltries were collected at the annual rendezvous, he would take them down to St. Louis, and bring back the needed supplies.

Jim decided not to renew his contract with the new company. He thought he would try his hand as a free trapper. In that way, his great energy and his skill as a trapper would be rewarded, because every pelt he brought in would bring the top price from the company or else be offered to a rival concern.

When the rendezvous broke up, Sublette found that he had on hand a large supply of goods which he and his partners had purchased from Ashley. It would be twelve long months before another rendezvous, and Bill's business sense recoiled at the thought of holding his merchandise that long. He decided to send it up into the

Blackfoot territory and try to sell it to those hostile Indians who did not attend the rendezvous. It was a daring scheme, but the Flatheads had reported that they and the Blackfeet were on good terms now, and that there would be no fighting with or killing of white men. It looked like a good time to cement friendship with the unpredictable Blackfeet.

"Who wants to go up to the Blackfoot country for me?" Sublette asked the trappers who still mulled around the rendezvous site.

Jim stepped forward, eager, as General Ashley had said, to undertake any venture which would dazzle his companions with its daring.

"I'll go, if I can take my friend Baptiste along," Jim offered, and the offer was accepted.

Sublette added another trapper to the undertaking for good measure, fitted the little party out with all the goods which the Indians loved, and bade them farewell.

The trio made their way into the disputed region, sold their goods to the eager Blackfeet, and within three weeks were on their way back with thirty-nine packs of beaver.

As a free trapper, Jim could go where he pleased, and he wished to stay close to Sublette's brigade. There were many reasons for this. Safety, of course, was one. But to Jim companionship was an even more powerful consideration. And in Sublette's brigade were many of Jim's friends: young Bridger, Robert Campbell, old Caleb Greenwood, and many others. So, though trapping on his own, he often camped with the hired trappers.

As autumn came on, Sublette divided his men into smaller brigades, sending them along the various streams to trap. Robert Campbell was made partisan of one such company, with young Bridger as his lieutenant. This

group was sent to trap along the Snake River, and Jim
went with it.

One night, while the men were sleeping peacefully, a
number of horses disappeared. Three of these belonged
to Jim and two to a companion named Alexander. As
there had been no sign of Indians, they decided their
horses had merely strayed away, and Campbell thought
it was safe enough for Jim and Aleck to go back to find
them.

The men traveled on foot along the back trail, keeping
an alert eye open for signs of the missing animals. On
the second day, rounding the shoulder of a hill, they
saw only a short distance ahead of them a band of Blackfeet also on foot. Aleck was panicky.

"I can't get away from them!" he cried. "I'm too old.
I can't make it! Jim, go! Go and leave me to my fate!"

"Look, Aleck!" Jim said urgently. "Try to get to the
creek and hide among the willows. I'll run out here in
plain sight. There's a chance they'll take after me, and
you can save yourself."

Aleck ran toward the willows and Jim, not waiting to
see how the man fared, turned and ran in full sight of
the Indians back toward the camp. Yelling, the Blackfeet took after him.

It was a race for life. Desperately aware that capture
meant certain death, perhaps preceded by torture, Jim
flew over the ground toward the buttes, where he expected to find his companions. Mile after mile he ran,
panting, almost fainting from thirst and weariness, but
kept going by his need to escape. He could see far ahead
of him the black outline of the buttes and this gave him a
little more strength; the sound of the pounding Indian
feet behind him renewed his faltering breath.

At last he came panting and stumbling around the

heel of the butte, ready to fall exhausted beside his friends. But no one was there—not a man, not a campfire, not a sign of those he had left. Appalled, Jim's eyes searched frantically, and saw the faint marks of a trail leading onward. Campbell had gone on.

Despairing, Jim set out along this trail. It was hopeless, he knew, but he could not bring himself to drop down and await death. Jim never knew how far he ran that day, but just when he could go no further, when his last ounce of strength was gone, he saw ahead of him the faint smoke of a campfire. At that moment, too, he was seen by the trappers, who ran forward to help him. The Indians, seeing the armed band, turned sullenly back and disappeared in the distance.

Jim was in terrible condition. His legs and feet were so swollen that for several days he could not stand on them. His whole body was wracked with aches and pains, until he almost felt that it would have been better to stay behind with Aleck and be scalped. For he was sure that was the fate of his companion.

A few days later, however, old Aleck came limping into camp, bemoaning the fact that poor Jim had been killed by the hostiles. He had passed a mutilated body, half-devoured by wolves, and was certain that it was Beckwourth's.

When the two men saw that they were both alive, they threw their arms about each other and wept with joy.

As the trappers moved on about their business they had many small encounters with Blackfeet and Bannocks, who seemed unable to let any band of white men pass unmolested. One of the worst battles was with a band of Bannocks who had killed two Snakes, and whom the trappers, therefore, were bound by the rules of the mountains to punish. They did so with a vengeance, bringing back more than a hundred Bannock scalps. This was an excuse for a great scalp dance and feast.

A band of Crows, hearing of the celebration, rode into camp to join the fun. They looked with envy on the flaunted scalps.

"Let us see the hero who brought down our enemies," they begged.

Jim had distinguished himself in the battle, but his companions were well aware that he would probably make his part shine out gloriously when it came to telling about the fight. Old Caleb Greenwood, whose wife was a Crow, could converse easily with his kinsmen, and he decided now to have a bit of fun with them at Jim's expense. He pointed to Jim.

"White-Handled Knife, there, is the real hero," he said, unsmiling. "His gun, his arrows, his white-handled knife have brung in more scalps than any other warrior."

The Crows stared at Jim. "How is it that a white man can be so brave and strong?" they asked.

Greenwood shook his head. "He ain't no white man! Can't you see that? Look at his skin! His hair! His eyes!"

The Crows looked. "What is he, then?"

"Why, dang it, can't you see? He's a Crow, that's what he is!"

The visitors gaped. "A Crow? How then is he with you white men?"

Caleb feigned surprise. "Don't you remember? Don't you recollect that big battle, many, many moons ago, when the Cheyennes defeated the Crows and ran away with many women and children? Jim, there, was one of them children. He was with the Cheyennes for a time, and then some white folks bought him and took him to St. Louie." Caleb's voice was serious, his eyes looked frankly into the eyes of his listeners. The other trappers did not have such complete control, but they managed to smother their chuckles and hide their smiles. Greenwood went on, "He's become a great brave among the white men, and his enemies fear him."

The Crows stared at Jim. They looked at each other. Then one spoke the words all were thinking, "He must come back to his people. He must come home with us!"

Jim, who had sat quietly by enjoying the fun, thought this might go beyond a good-natured joke. But he was willing to play Caleb's game a little longer. He shook his head and said seriously, "I can't leave my friends. I owe the white man much for saving me from the wicked Cheyennes. I must remain with them."

"No!" the Crows were equally determined, "you must return to Absaroka, to the land of your people. The old women have mourned for their lost sons. Now one of them will be made happy again."

Jim, of course, could not be persuaded, and at last the Crows left.

"Our people will be joyful," they said, "to know that we have found one bar-car-ta-a—a child of our tribe— who was stolen by the Cheyennes. The old women will rejoice that one whom they thought dead is still alive. But they will mourn that he does not return."

As the Crows rode away, the trappers could no longer conceal their merriment. They roared with laughter, rolled on the ground shouting. They pounded Jim, calling him Chief and Heap Big Crow. Jim chuckled too. The joke had ended happily, though for a few moments he had been just a bit worried.

Now Campbell moved his brigade up to the Powder River and across the Wind River Mountains into the land of the Crows. This pleased Jim. The Crows might steal a white man's horses, if the occasion seemed propitious, but they did not kill and scalp the trappers without due provocation. The constant vigilance maintained in the Blackfoot country could be relaxed. The trappers could get a good night's sleep without fear of losing their hair.

One night Jim set his six traps as usual. This job had become almost second nature to him by now. It required wading upstream for some distance, to avoid leaving any human odor on the rocks and bushes of the bank. The steel trap, which weighed some five pounds, was planted in shallow water a short distance from the shore. A long strong chain attached to the trap was fastened to a stick, which the trapper drove into the stream bed. Above the trap was fastened a twig on which had been smeared some of the castor, or musk, taken from the glands of trapped beavers.

When a trap was set successfully, there was nothing —no odor, no disturbed branches—to warn the beaver that his enemy had been near. He would smell the musk, swim out and reach up to grasp the baited twig in his strong teeth. This act would cause his feet to strike the trap, springing it, and he would be caught. For awhile he would struggle desperately, but the chain would hold him fast, and usually, after awhile, he would sink exhausted to the bottom and drown. Sometimes, however, the beaver would break the chain and drag the trap away, or he might gnaw off his leg, if but one foot was caught, and thus escape, mutilated but fighting.

When Jim went out one morning to "raise his traps" he found that he had caught four beaver, one trap was empty, and one was missing. He hunted up and down the stream, expecting to find where a beaver had managed to get away, but he could find no trap. When he returned to camp and told of the mysterious disappearance, his comrades agreed that it was a real puzzle.

The next day the brigade moved on. Thinking to save time, Jim and Bridger decided not to follow the stream but to cut across the intervening knolls and meet their companions later. And there, some distance from the camp, they found a dead beaver with Jim's trap securely fastened onto his hind legs.

Jim scratched his head, puzzled. "Now how d'you suppose he ever could have got here? He couldn't travel with that trap on his legs."

"And there's your float pole, too, Jim. How'd that git here?" puzzled Bridger.

Suddenly Jim grinned. "I'll bet a buffalo went through that stream, got tangled in the chain, and came charging along with my old beaver and trap on one side of his shoulders and the float pole on the other. Then, about here, he managed to shake loose of both of them."

They thought it was a good story, and one worth retelling at the campfire, but as Jim related the story, he managed to anger one of the trappers, by stating mysteriously that his trap had been stolen. The trapper, thinking Jim looked accusingly at him, jumped to his feet and challenged Jim to a fight. Jim, as touchy as the next one, did not bother to explain, and the fight was on.

Now there was confusion in the camp, some taking Jim's side, some standing by the aggrieved trapper. Bridger spoke quietly to the angry Beckwourth.

"Come on, Jim. Let's git out o' here fer a few days—till these fellers cool off a bit. Let's take our traps and git along upstream alone——"

Sulkily Jim consented and the two friends set out. They went upstream until they came to a fork.

"I'll take this here fork," Bridger suggested, "an' ye

take that one. Whomsoever gits his traps set fust can cross over that there ridge and meet t'other one, eh?"

Jim nodded and started off alone. His head was down, his thoughts resentfully churning in his mind. So absorbed was he in his unhappiness that he did not keep his usual alert lookout. He was brought up short when he found himself in the midst of a band of horses. He saw at a glance that these were not wild animals. Almost at the same moment he perceived that they were in the charge of an Indian horse guard who had seen him. It was too late to avoid them; Jim waited resolutely as the guards surrounded him.

As they drew nearer Jim saw with relief that they were Crows. He did not anticipate any rough treatment at their hands, and was surprised when they demanded his gun and traps and other equipment. Then, as if he were a prisoner, they began to march him toward the Crow village. In the distance, on the ridge, Jim could see his companion silhouetted against the sky. But Bridger was too far away to understand any signal he might make. There was nothing to do except march along with his captors. Jim, however, was puzzled by their air of triumph, the boisterous happiness of his captors. It seemed that they were acting as if they had caught a rare prize.

When they reached the village, the Crows hustled Jim straight to the chief's lodge.

And now he was able to understand his situation. Some braves came in, looked him over, and nodded. Jim recognized the young men to whom Caleb Greenwood had told his fantastic story. One of these who could speak English stepped close to Jim.

"We welcome you, my brother! Now you have come back to your people! The hearts of the old women will be glad." He turned to the others and explained, "This is the Crow who was stolen by the Cheyennes many winters ago, at the time of the big raid when the Crows were defeated. His arm is strong. He has killed many of our enemies. Now he has returned to his people."

Jim smiled wryly. He had returned because he couldn't help it. Well, they would soon discover their mistake and let him go.

The chief studied Jim sharply. Then he gave an order. Jim understood enough Crow to know that he had sent out for the women who had lost sons in that long-ago raid.

Soon the lodge was filled with old women. They began to examine Jim, looking for some mark that they could remember which would identify him as their son. His arms, his neck, his legs, face, hands, all were scrutinized with an intensity and a seriousness that made Jim realize for the first time how little of a joke this was with these people.

At last one old woman said, "If he is my son, he has a mole over one eye."

Immediately several hands took hold of Jim's eyelids and stretched them out as far as the skin would go, while black eyes studied the skin. Someone shrieked and pointed, and the old woman bent closer. There it was! On Jim's left eyelid there was a small brown mole.

A wild clatter of joy filled the tent. The old Crow woman seized Jim in her arms and embraced him, babbling words of endearment and joy. The others drew back, satisfied that Jim's mother had been found; ready to relinquish their own hopes and to rejoice in the good fortune of their friend.

When Jim's newly found mother's excitement abated a little, she took him by the hand and led him through the village to the lodge of her husband, Big Bowl, another chieftain. There she explained what had happened, pulled out Jim's eyelid and showed the telltale mole. Big Bowl accepted the proof as readily as his wife had done. He called together all his family to welcome their brother. It was a large family, with many pretty "sisters" and some fine, strapping "brothers," all of whom welcomed Jim with embraces and shrill exclamations.

The sisters made Jim sit down while they removed his worn and dirty moccasins and leggings, his tattered buckskin shirt. They brought new clothes—all of the finest buckskin, beautifully adorned with beads and elk teeth and porcupine quills. They dressed their newly found brother in these elegant clothes.

"Your name is Morning Star!" Big Bowl told him proudly. "You do not remember, but that is your name."

Jim accepted all this with mixed feelings. He was glad that he was being treated so well—it wasn't every day that a trapper came into a new outfit so easily. And it would be a hilarious story to tell his companions when he got back to camp. If he ever did get back! But there was danger, too. If these trusting people ever discovered that this was just a white man's hoax, his life would not be worth a coyote's bark. Yet what could he do? If he protested, they would not believe him. Had not Caleb Greenwood told them that Jim was a Crow? And Caleb spoke with a straight tongue.

When Jim's sisters had made him as elegant as possible, Big Bowl began to ask questions about Jim's life among the white man. Jim could understand fairly well, and there was the young Crow interpreter to help. This, with the universally understood sign language in which Jim was adept, made it possible for Big Bowl and his long-lost son to converse.

For ten days the village celebrated Jim's home-coming. There was dancing and feasting and singing. Almost every time he sat down for a moment, his mother or sisters would appear with a big bowl of dog soup, sure that Jim had missed this dainty while living among the white men.

At first Jim's stomach revolted at the thought of the dog soup, but after awhile he saw that his refusal to partake of their favorite dish was causing consternation, and he made himself eat it noisily and smack his lips in appreciation.

As the days went by, and Jim accepted more and more of the adulation and gifts, he knew that he was getting involved in something that he could not lightly escape. And, he had to admit to himself, he did not know that he wanted to escape. Never in his life had he been treated with the respect and admiration now lavished upon him. He had always longed for just such approbation—and now here it was, showered upon him.

And it might be a smart move to sit tight and take whatever came. Studying the situation, Jim had to admit that as a Crow he would be in an excellent position to obtain peltries from his "relatives" at the very lowest price, or for no payment at all. Here, after all these years, all these hardships, might be his very chance to obtain the fortune he had so long desired.

Sitting in Big Bowl's lodge, smoking, being treated like a king, Jim's thoughts were busy. Finally he shrugged. He had made his decision—not that any other was practical at this time. He would take all that was offered and in return he would give his new relatives no cause to grumble at their chief's son.

CHAPTER 9

Jim Makes Good

After ten days, when the rejoicing over Morning Star's return to Absaroka had quieted down a bit, Jim found that he was to all intents and purposes a full-fledged member of the tribe. He had been offered and had accepted Blue Flower, a subchief's daughter, as his wife. He smiled wryly at the gift, but it was one he could not refuse without insulting his new "relatives." It was unthinkable to the Crows that a chief's son of Jim's age should have no wife. Jim also had his own lodge piled high with buffalo robes given to him as welcoming gifts. He had an elegant wardrobe, several horses, guns, ammunition—everything that befitted the son of Big Bowl.

Jim accepted his new status with the coolness of the seasoned trapper toward any unexpected situation. Here in the mountains, where death rode beside every pony and lurked behind every bush, men met each day's adventures with the action that seemed most expedient at the moment. It was impossible to plan too far ahead, and necessary only to live each day through. Jim gave little thought to the reaction of his trapper companions. He knew their attitude: when a man disappeared or was rubbed out they shrugged and went on about their work. As long as a companion was living, they would risk their own lives willingly on his behalf. Once he was gone, there was no use to waste time over him. Only Baptiste, Jim knew, would truly miss him and mourn for him. Perhaps, too, his father.

The Crows, on their part, accepted Jim joyfully. It seemed to them a good omen that this lost child should be returned. They invited him to go on a horse-stealing raid. Jim understood that to an Indian, horse stealing was not the same thing that it was to a white man. All Indians stole horses as a way of life. There was nothing reprehensible about it. Rather, it was the most accept-able method of winning acclaim and honor. Jim knew that he could not refuse so generous an invitation. He joined a raiding party of forty, headed by young Red Elk.

The band traveled for three days without sighting an enemy. Then, in a wide valley ahead, they spied a band of Blackfeet. Red Elk immediately ordered a charge. The Crows lifted their lances, kicked their horses' flanks, and went swooping and yelling straight for the enemy. The Blackfeet drew up in battle line and awaited the onslaught.

Jim felt wild exhilaration pound through his veins. Yelling with the others, he galloped ahead, the excite-ment of the battle taking complete control of his senses. The line of Crows swept on almost up to the Blackfeet. Then, without warning or hesitation, the Crow line broke in the center. Half galloped away to the right, half to the left, without shooting a single arrow or firing a single shot.

Unaware of what was happening, Jim rushed straight at the enemy, firing his gun. He saw his target throw up his hands and scream, then slide to the ground. Jim glanced about him and found that he was alone amid the scalp-hungry, bloodthirsty Blackfeet. But he was stranded for only a moment. As soon as the astounded Crows saw what had happened, they wheeled and came back to rescue their brother.

This maneuver surprised the enemy, who understood the first feint, which was the accepted Indian tactic, but could not comprehend this about-face They broke ranks and scattered. The surprise attack of the Crows resulted in other casualties among the startled Blackfeet.

Jim was the hero of the hour. He had brought down the first man, had taken the first coup—this was a great honor. The Crows praised him, but did not let that delay their scalping operations. Then, painting their faces black to indicate victory, the triumphant little band rode joyously back to the village, carrying their loot with them.

The Crows at home heard the singing and came out to welcome the heroes. Jim gave his wife the gun he had taken from his victim. To his "sisters" he gave Blackfoot lances and arrows. Singing and dancing, they all entered the village and made ready to enjoy a great scalp dance. Because Jim had brought down the first enemy, his entire shirt was painted black and he was given the place of honor as first coup striker.

Big Bowl, in honor of his son's triumph, gave away all of his horses and other property. Jim was saddened to see the old man made penniless just because his son had proved a hero. But it was the Crow custom and must be observed.

The entire village took part in the rejoicing. The bodies of the braves were painted with charcoal and buffalo blood, white clay and vermilion. They wore their finest clothing, decorated with beads and feathers, furs and scarlet cloth. The women and children donned their finest apparel; the horses had bunches of turkey feathers on their tails and strips of scarlet cloth tied to their manes. Even the ugly, wolfish looking dogs were dressed up with bunches of feathers and strips of bright cloth.

The dancers were divided into small bands according to some tribal distinction. Jim watched the dancers for awhile before joining in. He wanted to attach himself to the group that contained the most active and daring young men. Deciding finally upon a certain set, he went over, broke into the circle and began dancing.

Immediately a joyous cry went up. "The great brave, the Antelope, has joined our band!" Jim heard his new name with satisfaction. It indicated a sort of promotion in the minds of his fellows, who bestowed a new name for every great honor a brave achieved.

For a time, now, Jim could devote himself to trapping. He had determined that this escapade should be the road to the fortune he had so long desired. After one year here, he thought, he could return to St. Louis as rich as General Ashley, for he would have an entire tribe working for him alone.

On his trapping excursions, Jim was often accompanied by a fine, intelligent young Crow named Bear-wolf. Bear-wolf was an orphan and had no relatives. He asked Jim to be his brother.

"I am your friend," Jim said, "and would like to be your blood brother, but that is impossible."

"No," Bear-wolf said, "it can be done. Here, you take all my traps and give me yours. Take my gun and ammunition, my horse and my clothing and give me yours in exchange."

Jim had easily adopted the policy of agreeing to any "honor" a Crow might wish to bestow upon him. It saved a good deal of difficulty. Now he traded everything he owned for Bear-wolf's possessions. Then Bear-wolf said,

"Now we are one. You and I are brothers. We must never leave the village at the same time. One must always stay behind to guard the possessions of the other."

Jim agreed, though he was a bit dubious about the arrangement. Bear-wolf had very little property while Jim owned a number of fine horses, and had guns and ammunition, buffalo robes, deerskins and other property. But that night, when Jim told Big Bowl what had happened, the old chief nodded his head.

"It is good. Bear-wolf is strong and brave and honest. Now he will take care of your property when you go out on the warpath."

Jim looked sharply at the old man. "The warpath?" he asked.

Big Bowl nodded. "A war party is being made up and you are to go with it, my son."

When Bear-wolf heard that Jim was going on the warpath he asked, "Have you been initiated into the warpath secret?"

Jim shook his head.

"You will be now. They will tell you tomorrow."

The war party set out the next morning. On their way they killed a fat buffalo and stopped for a feast. After the best cuts had been roasted and eaten, some of the older warriors took a part of the animal's intestines, washed them and made a long, slender sausage. This was brought to Jim's mess, which consisted of ten men. They stood up and formed a circle, each one taking hold of the sausage with his thumb and forefinger—a position felt to be sacred by the Crows, and anything said while standing thus was considered as being under oath.

Now the captain began to ask questions about the personal conduct of each soldier. Each answered in turn, fully and honestly, though sometimes with shame. Every dishonorable act, whether great or trivial, committed since the last raid was brought to light. All would be reported to the medicine man upon the return of the party. All would be recorded and kept forever against the wrongdoer's name.

When it came Jim's turn he was told that this was the warpath secret.

"You must swear never to reveal what you hear!" the captain warned. "Swear it upon your gun, your pipe, your knife. Swear it upon the earth and the sun!"

Jim took the oath and then answered the captain's questions. As he did so he was thinking: Now I am getting deeper and deeper into this life. How can I escape? If I tell them I am not a Crow they will not believe me. I will just have to go along until I see my way clear to escape.

After the ritual they made a successful raid upon an Assiniboin village. Jim's share of the loot was seventeen horses. The Crows managed this without suffering any losses, themselves, so they returned in great glory. Jim was able to give Big Bowl a number of animals to replace those the chief had given away in his son's honor.

"You have done well, my son," Big Bowl said proudly. "Your medicine is strong. Now you must head a war party."

Jim hesitated. It was one thing to steal horses and quite another to go out deliberately to kill an unsuspecting enemy, who was, after all, no enemy of Jim's.

Big Bowl went on, "That is the next step on the path of honor. Already you have accomplished the first three: You have touched an enemy. You have struck the first blow in an encounter. You have snatched the weapon from the hand of your foe. Now you must plan and lead a war party. Then all will know that you have not been spoiled by the white man. You will set your feet on the path to glory."

It was a tempting idea. He had worked hard for General Ashley and had not been rewarded with the captaincy of six men on a trapping expedition. Here he had done nothing extraordinary and was already being urged to command a war party. A feeling of affection for these people began to grow in Jim's heart.

"It is the way to win promotion," Bear Wolf urged. "Your brother-in-law, Black Panther, wishes to go with you. You can select your own party. You have strong medicine and will be fortunate."

Jim was frowning thoughtfully. So far he had had good luck, and the Crows attributed good luck to the special favor of the Great Spirit—to strong medicine. But would his luck hold out? And what would happen if it failed? There was no escape, however, from the trial.

"Very well," he told Big Bowl. "I shall go."

He knew it would be thought presumptuous for him to ask experienced warriors to go out on his initial raid, so he selected seven youths, ranging in age from ten to seventeen. They were delighted to be introduced to the warpath by the powerful Antelope.

Jim decided to invade the land of the Arapaho, traditional enemies of the Crows. His party journeyed southward toward the headwaters of the Arkansas. Jim moved cautiously, because he was eager to return with his band intact. And finally, his scouts reported that there was an Arapaho village not far away. The men were out hunting and the women were busy at their tasks, unsuspicious of any danger.

With the greatest caution and secrecy Jim deployed his men around the horses, which were quietly grazing a short distance from the lodges of the Arapaho. When all were in position, Jim gave a war whoop, and spurred his horse from its ambush. The others rode out of hiding, yelling and shouting, stampeding the horses, and sending them galloping along the back trail.

Taken completely by surprise, the Arapaho women came yelling and screaming, flinging rocks and imprecations upon the thieves. Jim laughed at them, but he kept moving. There could be no rest until they were far enough away to be somewhat safe from the revengeful Arapoho, who would certainly try to get back their animals, and maybe a Crow scalp or two to boot.

His party had captured nearly a hundred horses, and they were so jubilant that they did not need to rest. They wanted to get back to their village and to the wild excitement of a triumphant return.

When the young warriors, their faces painted black, their voices loud in song, approached the village, there was pandemonium. Many of the horses Jim had stolen were recognized as Crow property, and a chant went up, "Great is Antelope! Great is the son of Big Bowl! None can stand against the Enemy-of-Horses!"

So now Jim had still another name; he had achieved the four great honors; he was ready to be a subchief.

There might possibly have been some delay before this honor was given to Jim if an incident had not happened at that moment.

The Crows were camped near a mountain, on the face of which was a large cave. A huge grizzly bear had taken over the cave as his home, from which he emerged to strike terror into the hearts of the Indians. No man, either white or red, sought combat with this killer of the West.

A small party of Crows, Jim among them, went out to kill the bear. They succeeded only in driving him back into his lair.

"Go in! Go in!" Jim shouted to his companions. "Let's go in and get him now! Now's the time!"

The braves stood back. "No man can kill him now," they said.

"Oh, this is the very time! He's driven to the wall. Go in—or some of you come with me! We'll get him!"

They stared at Jim as if he were crazy. They said it was impossible. These words, this attitude, were the very things to stimulate Jim to rashness.

"Well, then," he said, "I will go in alone. I will show you that Enemy-of-Horses is Enemy-of-Bears as well."

Jim stripped off his clothing. Then taking a heavy Mexican blanket from one of the bystanders, he wrapped it over his left arm. In his right hand he grasped his stout white-handled knife. Without a glance at the shuddering Crows, he entered the cave.

To the watchers it seemed as if Jim must have been killed, as the moments dragged by and he did not reappear. They could hear sounds of scuffling, grunts and groans, but none that could be distinguished as the death cry. Yet he must be dead. They looked at each other sorrowfully. It was a tragic ending to a brave, but foolish, act.

Just then Jim appeared at the mouth of the cave. He was torn and bleeding, his long hair matted with sweat and blood. In his hand he still held the knife, now dripping gore. Jim stooped and wiped the knife blade on the grass.

"Old Grizzly's dead," he said calmly.

The Crows went wild. They began to chant praise of Jim's valor and prowess.

"He is the greatest coup striker among the Crows!"
Black Panther cried. "He must be a subchief. We have
no greater brave!"

And so Jim was elevated to the council of the chief-
tains; he now could carry a shield with his device upon
it. Jim chose as his symbol a green bird sitting between
the horns of a crescent, with a star on each side of the
field. Many braves offered to help make and paint the
shield of buffalo hide, and it proved to be a very strik-
ing object when it was done.

During the winter the Crow village was raided several times by Sioux, Blackfeet, Arikaras, and Arapaho.
But each time the Crows sent out retaliatory expeditions,
which seemed always to be triumphant. Of course, from
time to time, Crow braves were slain. Then the village
went into mourning. The wives of the slain men cut off
their fingers; they tore out their hair; they screamed with
sorrow and painted their faces with ashes. When the
bodies could be recovered, they were wrapped in scarlet
cloth and placed in treetops until the flesh had all decayed away. Then the bones were taken down and in-
terred in a cave.

In midwinter Jim sent some peltries down to the
trading post to be bartered for certain goods he wanted.
Each of his pelts was marked J. B. This caused a good
deal of excitement at the post as the trader James Kipp,
could not understand how any Crow could initial his
furs. Jim chuckled when the returning travelers told him
of the incident.

In March a war party of twenty Crows went out. Not
one of them returned. Their war dogs, stripped of the
packs they carried for their masters, came limping back
to the village, hungry and gaunt. When the Crows saw
these emaciated animals they knew that the entire party

had been murdered by one of the hostile tribes. Only the dogs had escaped, and with unerring instinct made their way home. The women went into mourning, but the warriors set out to get revenge.

Jim was chosen to lead this party, and again his "medicine" proved powerful. They followed the trail of the victors to their camp, surprised them unprepared, and killed them all. They retrieved the Crow property and horses, and returned. The mourning was immediately transformed into a jubilant scalp dance.

About this time an incident occurred which intensified the Crows' faith in Jim's "medicine," or mystical power. During an enemy attack Jim was struck by a bullet. It knocked him to the ground, and when he tried to rise, blood spurted from his mouth. The Crows were sure that their hero had been mortally wounded. They made Jim lie down and started to remove his clothes. The flattened bullet fell to the ground.

Amazed, the braves drew back and stared at this. Then they looked at Jim, who now got to his feet unaided.

"The Enemy-of-Horses cannot be harmed by bullets!" Black Panther said in awe.

Jim said nothing. He realized that the bullet had hit the hilt of his hunting knife. But it was just as well to have this aura of mysticism about him. He mounted his horse, waved his gun, gave his battle cry, and galloped off after the fleeing Cheyennes.

CHAPTER 10

Chief of the Crows

By the time Jim was made a subchief, it was impossible for a casual observer to distinguish any difference between him and his companions. He wore his buckskin attire easily, and was proud of its decorations, each one of which signified some special honor he had earned. As coup striker, the first to bring down an enemy in a raid, Jim wore wolf tails at the heels of his moccasins. Because he had snatched a gun from the enemy, he was entitled to trim his shirt with ermine skins. As a leader of a successful war party, his leggings were fringed with ermine and scalps. Blue Flower followed him, carrying with pride his circular buffalo-hide shield with its device of bird and crescent.

Jim now had several Indian wives. With every promotion, a new wife was offered to the hero. He accepted the gift, placed the bride in a lodge of her own and brought her trophies from his battles. But only to Blue Flower was accorded the signal honor of carrying his shield, for, though Jim acceded to the Crow custom, he regarded Black Panther's sister as his true wife. And, as yet, none of his wives had presented him with a child.

Week by week, month by month, Jim found it easier and easier to adopt the Crow customs. Inwardly, he began to think and feel like a Crow. He still reacted at

times to his early training: He did what he could to pre-
vent the sale of rum and whisky to his tribesmen; he
strenuously objected to attacks on white traders or travelers, which did occur at times in spite of the traditional
Crow friendship for the white man. And, alone, he observed a day in midwinter as Christmas, recalling his
years in the Catholic school and the holy nature of the
day.

Reports of the strange Crow brave, who could not be
killed by bullets and who possessed such powerful medicine against his enemies, began to filter through the
Northwest. No one suspected that the mysterious chief
was Jim Beckwourth, the trapper, until he had been in
the Crow village for more than two years. He had been
captured by the Crows early in 1827. In the fall of 1829
he left the village to go down to Fort Clark, in the
Mandan country, to trade his peltries for needed supplies. With him went a small party of his companions.

They deposited their peltries and began to make their
purchases. As was the Indian custom, a man would lay
out a pelt, then point to the goods he wanted. When he
had obtained as much as the trader would allow for that
pelt, it would be tossed onto the trader's pile of furs.
Another pelt would be laid out, and its value purchased.
It was a slow and tedious process, but no one could
hurry it along.

Jim stood back, watching the proceedings, but saying
nothing. Finally Black Panther asked for "be-has-i-pe-
hish-a."

The clerk did not understand what was wanted, and as
there was none of the stuff in sight, Black Panther was at
a loss how to make his want known. After a good deal of
haggling, the clerk called James Kipp, who had estab-

lished the post some years before. Kipp listened to Black
Panther, and shook his head. He, too, was mystified.

Then Jim spoke up. "Gentlemen, that Indian wants
some scarlet cloth."

Kipp and his clerk stared at hearing these well-spoken
English words coming from the mouth of a Crow.

"Ah," the clerk said when he had mastered his amaze-
ment, "you speak English. Where did you learn it?"

Jim grinned. "With the white man in St. Louis."

"And how long were you with the white man?"

"Twenty years," Jim said, enjoying the impact he was
making.

Now Kipp broke in. "If you were in St. Louis for
twenty years you are no Crow."

"No," Jim agreed, "I am not. My name is Jim Beckwourth!" He said the last proudly, conscious of his prestige among the Crows.

If his first words in English had caused a stir, his name
exploded like a bombshell. Kipp rushed forward and examined Jim closely. Then he cried, "Good heavens! I
have heard of you often! You are supposed to be dead.
Captain Sublette reported that you were killed by Cheyennes more than two years ago. You must be the Crow
who sent down the peltries marked J.B.!"

"I am," Jim said. "And now, Mr. Kipp, I have been
watching your clerks deal with my brothers. Your men
have seen to it that you have made two to three hundred
per cent profit on every peltry. I don't begrudge you that.
Perhaps, in your place, I'd do the same thing. But I have
worked hard and suffered many dangers to obtain my
peltries, and I don't aim to be cheated. I want full value
for every one."

Kipp nodded. He knew that if Jim chose to expose his

cheating to the Indians there might be real trouble. He advised his clerks to give Jim full value for every pelt. The Crows stood around staring as Jim's pile of goods mounted higher and higher.

Black Panther frowned, trying to understand why Jim was treated so much better than his companions. Suddenly his face cleared and he exclaimed, "Ugh! I see it now! The white man pays you for the captivity you suffered among them!"

Jim grinned and let it go at that. But he turned to Kipp.

"Tell me what was reported about my death," he said.

"Well," Kipp answered, "Jim Bridger saw you taken captive by a party of Indians. He was too far away to distinguish what tribe they were, but he took them to be Cheyennes. When he saw you give up your gun and traps he knew you were a prisoner. He returned to camp and reported to Captain Sublette, and when no word came from you, it was supposed you had been killed."

Jim shrugged. "Well now you can tell anyone who is interested that I am still alive. I am a subchieftain among the Crows, and I intend to remain there for some time."

"Until you make a fortune from their furs, eh?" Kipp suggested slyly.

Jim returned to the Crow village and distributed presents right and left. He was unaware that the announcement he had made so arrogantly would redound to his discredit during the next few years. For now the white men, who were infiltrating the Northwest in greater and greater numbers, had someone to blame for every Indian misdeed. They had been aware of the great success of the Crows in their offensive and defensive battles in the immediate past. Now it was all accounted for. They were no longer dependent on Indian strategy, laziness and ignorance. They had the help of a shrewd, intelligent and ruthless man who understood white men's tactics and could outguess them.

About this time Jim became acquainted with a Crow maiden who was superior in looks, intelligence and desirability to any other Crow woman he had yet met. The young woman's name was Bar-chee-am-pa, or Pine Leaf, and she was held in the highest esteem by all the Crows.

Pine Leaf's twin brother had been killed while defending the village against a Cheyenne attack. At that time, the twins were mere youngsters, but Pine Leaf had taken a vow that she would never rest or marry until she had killed a hundred of the enemy to pay for her beloved brother's death. Since then she had become a warrior, and rode out with war parties against the Cheyennes. When Jim met her she was a handsome young woman, strong, courageous and intelligent. Many a Crow brave wished that she would soon accomplish her vow, so that he might claim her as his bride.

Jim shared this wish. For the first time he had found a Crow woman who more nearly fitted the civilized notion of a wife: someone who could be a real companion; whose intelligence, courage and spirit matched his own. He had accepted his other wives simply to avoid insulting his tribesmen; he had not chosen them, himself. With Pine Leaf it was different; he wanted to win her as his wife.

Pine Leaf asked Jim to let her become one of his Dog Soldiers. He was delighted to accept her offer, for this would give him many opportunities to press his suit. The heroine liked Jim, but she treated his proposals with good-natured humor. Once she told him that she would marry him when the leaves above their heads turned brown. Jim was happy for a moment, until he realized that they were riding under pine trees. Again, Pine Leaf said she would marry Jim when he captured a red-headed Indian, and again he knew that she was laughing at him. In spite of all this, however, she rode beside her captain on many a raid and proved herself a brilliant warrior. In several frays she managed to protect Jim, and sometimes even to save his life.

In the winter of 1831-32, Jim received a letter from Kenneth McKenzie, who was in charge of Fort Union at the mouth of the Yellowstone. This was a post of John Jacob Astor's American Fur Company, which was threatening to take over the entire fur trade of the Northwest, driving the smaller companies out of business. Astor's company was the bitter rival of the Rocky Mountain Fur Company, owned by Jim's companions of his Ashley days. McKenzie's autocratic handling of affairs had earned him the title "King of the Upper Missouri." A letter from him was not to be ignored. Jim packed a parfleche with necessary supplies and set out to answer the summons.

He arrived safely at Fort Union and was ushered into the great factor's presence. Immediately he became conscious of his own unkempt appearance, for McKenzie was immaculate in a fine uniform, brilliant with gold braid and military decorations. His aristocratic manner and haughty assurance were such as Jim had not met since he had said good-by to General Ashley. McKenzie, too, seemed conscious of their difference in status, for he did not ask Jim to sit down, but spoke curtly, as to an inferior. Jim bristled at the man's manner, but his years among the Indians had taught him a valuable lesson in self-control.

"I have here at the fort an immense supply of goods,"

McKenzie began. "Perhaps you know that now we can send steamships loaded with goods up the Missouri, so that we have more than has ever before been brought into Indian territory. Now I want to establish a trading post among the Crows, and I have sent for you, Beckwourth, to suggest that you undertake the project. I know your reputation," he said dryly, "and I think you are just the man for me. You would be an employe of the American Fur Company, at a fixed wage, with extra compensation for superior accomplishment. What do you say, sir?"

Jim hesitated. He had guessed from McKenzie's letter what would be suggested, and he had decided what he would do. But he did not want to appear eager. His great schemes for getting rich from the trapping activities of the Crows had not come to much. The Indians hated to trap, except for the pelts and food they required. To trap for others seemed silly, indeed. They would much rather fight or steal horses.

Jim had argued the point over and over again, but the answer was always the same: "Our enemies steal our horses and we must steal them back, or we will perish. How can we make a buffalo surround without horses?" or "Our enemies kill our brothers. Our brothers' spirits can find no rest until they are avenged. We must fight."

Now, Jim was thinking, if he was backed by this company which, as every trapper knew, was gradually devouring the entire fur business, he would not only have a guaranteed wage, but he would have more authority for getting the Indians to work. In return, he might be able to help his tribesmen by seeing that they were treated fairly. At the same time he was fully aware that he was joining a hated company.

"Well, sir?" McKenzie asked impatiently.

"I will accept the offer, sir," Jim answered coolly, "providing the terms are satisfactory."

"I'll make them satisfactory," McKenzie said curtly.

By nightfall the deal was settled, and the next morning Jim set out on the homeward trail with ten pack horses loaded with goods. In addition to this, McKenzie was to send several boatloads up the Yellowstone, with fifty men to build his post in Absaroka.

Jim had scarcely returned to the Crows and explained his new position, making it sound very important to his listeners, than Samuel Tulloch arrived with the boats and men and the building of the new post, Fort Cass, began.

This move of Jim's was not likely to endear him to the owners of the smaller companies, nor to the trappers who worked for them. Actually, it was considered with deep repugnance and anger by many of the white men who felt that the great Astor company was using unfair tactics in taking over the fur trade. It was bad enough, they muttered to each other, that Jim Beckwourth chose to live among the Crows, inciting these former friends to all sorts of wickedness against the whites. Now that he had gone over to the Astor company, they could expect almost any evil. Jim's position as a subchief laid him open to suspicion; his job as agent for the hated company made all those suspicions seem true. Among the white men in the region, Jim now was blamed for every Indian raid, every loss of pelts or horses; and later, even for the smallpox epidemic that nearly wiped out the Mandans and worked terrible havoc among the neighboring tribes.

Jim was unaware of the growing resentment against him. He had been promoted to first counselor in the Crow nation, only a step below the great war chief,

A-ra-poo-ash, or Rotten Belly. He had his hands full managing the affairs of his adopted people and conducting the business of his new employers. In the fall of 1832 a clash between Indians and white men occurred which seemed to prove that Jim had turned renegade, and opened his eyes to the reputation he had acquired.

Captain Benjamin Louis Eulalie de Bonneville arrived in the West that fall with a large company of trappers, army men, servants and wagons loaded with supplies. The captain, ostensibly on an exploring expedition halfheartedly sponsored by the government, was in reality out to make a fortune for himself in the fur business. He had absolutely no idea how to treat the Indians, and no thought that one tribe was different from another. To Captain Bonneville, all Indians were thieves and murderers and were to be treated exactly as rattlesnakes.

A small brigade of Bonneville's men had some trouble with a band of Crows that came into their camp. One man was killed. Adams, the captain of the brigade, reported to Bonneville that a mulatto had been the leader of the Indians. Bonneville immediately sent an emissary to Rotten Belly, accusing Jim and demanding reparation.

During his years among the Crows, where he was treated with so much honor and respect, Jim had practically forgotten the heritage that had clouded his childhood. He was amazed and shocked when Bonneville immediately suspected him to be the mulatto who had led the attack.

Jim denied all knowledge of the raid, and laid the blame on High Lance, a bad Indian, and his band. This small, rebellious group included a dozen renegade white trappers and a mulatto to whom High Lance had given shelter. Jim managed to find in the village a part of Bonneville's stolen property, but his denial of participation in the attack was not believed by the captain, who took every occasion thereafter to vilify Jim's reputation.

"Beckwourth created the raid in order to steal my furs for his employer!" Bonneville asserted, starting a rumor that Jim never quite lived down.

Jim, overwhelmed with resentment and anger, sat brooding in his lodge one day. The blanket over the door opening was lifted and Blue Flower came in, carrying a bundle. Jim paid no attention at first, and his wife came nearer. She held up the bundle, which Jim now saw was a cradleboard on which was strapped a baby.

Blue Flower spoke softly. "Here is something that will gladden your heart. He will make as great a brave as his father. His name is Black Panther. Here, look at your son."

For a moment Jim scarcely comprehended what the woman had said. He stared from her to the infant. Then, as realization swept over him, he felt a great wave of emotion, a feeling he had never before known, in which tenderness and exultation mingled. He reached out awkwardly and took the child in his arms and stared down into the wide, unblinking eyes.

"My son!" he murmured, "future chief of the Crows!" Bonneville and his accusations were forgotten, and preparations for a feast of rejoicing were immediately begun.

In September of the following year, Jim was camped with his Indians on the Tongue River when he heard that a party of trappers led by Broken Hand was camped nearby. Jim had not seen Fitzpatrick for years and was eager to talk to his old friend. Though Tom was now the head of the rival Rocky Mountain Fur Company, Jim decided to visit his former companion.

Before he could get away, however, Tom came into the village demanding to see Rotten Belly, who had long been a friend. Jim had just returned from a foray with his Dog Soldiers. He saw Tom, but for a moment did not recognize him. The Irishman's thick sandy hair was now snow-white. As soon as Jim recognized the features below the white hair, he rushed forward.

But Fitzpatrick either didn't see Jim, or didn't recognize him. He rode past his old friend, and Jim noticed then that the honest Irish face was dark with anger. Beside him rode a frowning man. They went straight to Rotten Belly's lodge and dismounted. Without ceremony, Tom entered the chieftain's lodge.

"What does this mean?" he roared. "While I was here visiting with you yesterday, a guest in your lodge, your warriors attacked my camp and stole everything they could lay their hands on, even to Captain Stewart's watch. Is this your boasted friendship, Rotten Belly?"

Jim, who had followed along behind the two angry men, could hear every word.

The old Chief was amazed. He told Tom to sit down and tell him what had happened. Fitzpatrick minced no words. While he had been visiting with Rotten Belly the day before, a band of Crows had descended upon his camp, where Captain Stewart was in charge. At first they pretended to be friends; they had laughed and joked with their white brothers. Then suddenly, when the trappers were all unsuspecting, knives had flashed, guns and lances had appeared from under blankets. The trappers were entirely at the mercy of their unbidden guests. They had to stand by and watch the Crows plunder the camp.

Rotten Belly was angry. "The Crows are friends of

the white man. It is true that we now trade our peltries
with the American company. It has built a post in Absaroka. It furnishes the Crow with all he needs."

"And some things he doesn't need," Fitzpatrick said
hotly, thinking of the still McKenzie was building at
Fort Union so that he could supply the Indians with for-
bidden liquor.

The old chief nodded wisely. Then he said, "I will re-
cover what I can of your goods."

He called Jim, as second in command, and put him in
charge of rounding up the horses and collecting the
stolen goods. Jim went through the village; he found only
a few horses and traps, but not a single peltry bearing
the familiar RMF brand. Nor did he find any of the
trade goods Fitzpatrick had brought to the region.

Tom took the pitiful remnants of his once rich outfit
and left the Crow country. He gave no friendly word
of parting to Jim. Instead, he looked at his one-time
companion with resentment and suspicion.

Jim needed no interpreter to explain that look. Fitzpatrick believed that Jim had instigated the raid in
order to obtain the peltries of the Rocky Mountain Fur
company for his own employers. And if Jim hadn't understood the look, Tom's companion, Captain William
Drummond Stewart, left him in no doubt. The Scotch
nobleman, who had served with Wellington at Waterloo,
looked at Jim with the utmost contempt and shouted,
"You are a damned rascal, Jim Beckwourth! You set your
Indians upon us. No one but a damned rascal would
live among this treacherous crew!"

The contempt of this famous soldier hurt Jim more
than he would admit. His dark face flushed and his fierce
black eyes burned with resentment. But he could not
answer. Stewart was a guest of the old chief.

The insult rankled and festered until it was a small, never-quite-forgotten sore deep in Jim's heart. A damned rascal? Well, his one-time friends might think so. He could do everything in his power to shield and protect them, but they would still believe him guilty of treachery. His Crow friends knew better. Their ardent admiration and deep respect was a soothing balm to Jim's hurt spirit. At that moment he thought he wouldn't care if he never saw a white man again.

Then a slow secret smile lifted the corners of Jim's lips. If the rival company thought he had done this for the benefit of the American Fur Company, it might be just as well to let his employer think so, too. When Tulloch sent down to Fort Union a pile of beaver peltries marked RMF, it was with the explanation that a severe blow had been dealt the rival company, which had now been driven from Absaroka.

Jim watched the boatloads of peltries float downstream, and then turned with greater eagerness to the activities of his adopted people.

CHAPTER 11

Civilization Beckons

※※

Jim had been among the Crows for nearly twelve "snows." Rotten Belly, the head chief, was old and sick, and Jim was virtually the leader of the tribe. He had almost forgotten his life among the white men. His honorary name now was Bloody Arm.

One day he was leading a large war party against the Blackfeet when Rotten Belly, heading a smaller party, caught up with him. Jim was shocked at the old chief's appearance, and knew that if he insisted on going to battle he would certainly be killed. He tried to dissuade the chief, pretending that his medicine told him the Great Spirit did not want them to go to battle at this time.

Rotten Belly would not listen. "You do not want me to fight," he said, "because you think I shall be killed. Well, I came here to die. I shall never return to the village. Look, I will give you a sign."

He placed the edge of his shield on some buffalo chips and said, "Warriors, you see my shield. If it rises, I shall die here."

He then lifted his face toward the sun and muttered some prayers. After this he took his lance and made some strange motions with it. Every warrior's eye was upon the intent old chief as he slowly raised the lance point from the shield toward the sun.

A cry of dismay escaped their lips, for, as the lance rose the shield, too, rose from the ground, hung poised for a moment, and then fell, clattering, back to earth. Jim sighed.

"The chief means to die in battle," he told himself. "So he manages this trick. But how he did it escaped me!"

Rotten Belly flung himself upon his horse and started away after a small band of Blackfeet that had been seen in the distance. Jim and the Crows followed at top speed, but some demon seemed to spur on the old man. He reached the Blackfeet first, dashed in among them, and began to lash right and left with his battle ax. He had struck two shrieking enemies from their horses when an arrow entered his body, passing through so that the tip showed between his shoulders.

The sight of their injured chief gave added fury to the oncoming Crows, who galloped in among the Blackfeet and slaughtered them all.

The Crows gathered around their dying chief. "Warriors," he said, "I came here to die. A-ra-poo-ash will lead you no more. Bloody Arm, come to me. You must take the place of A-ra-poo-ash. You are strong and brave and wise. Your medicine is powerful. You, Bloody Arm, are the only brave who can keep the nation together. Bloody Arm, listen!"

"I hear you," Jim answered.

Rotten Belly sighed deeply, then went on with great effort, "Tell Nam-i-ne-dishee, the wife that I have always loved, to tell my sons who their father was. Do not let them forget. Let my body be buried on this spot. I can hear the voice of the Great Spirit. He calls for A-ra-poo-ash to come to the Spirit Land. I must go."

With these last words the old chief died. The warriors gathered around and set up such a lamentation as Jim had never before heard.

As he had been designated chief by Rotten Belly, Jim immediately took command of the situation. He sent a herald to the village to inform the people that A-ra-poo-ash was dead. Then he had a grave dug and buried the chief according to his wishes, although this type of burial was not according to the usual Crow procedure.

The war party now turned its steps homeward, moving slowly and solemnly. When they drew in sight of the village they saw that every lodge had been stricken and lay flat on the ground. Shrieks, cries and yells of sorrow surrounded them. Blood was streaming from the bodies of every mourning Crow. Hundreds of fingers were cut off; hanks of hair torn from their heads lay about the paths. Jim shuddered at the fearful sight and the dolorous sounds.

The mourning for the great chief lasted two days. Then Jim ordered the village moved over to the Rosebud river. There a council lodge was built, the national records were gone over by the medicine men, and a lengthy consultation was held. At its conclusion, it was announced that Jim had been elected First Counselor and that he was to rule conjointly with Long Hair as first chief of the nation.

Long Hair was well named. His black hair was more than nine feet long. He wore it braided and bound with a strap, and folded into a buckskin pouch which he wore under his arm. On special occasions he unbraided his hair and let it hang loose. When Rotten Belly died, Long Hair did something he had never before done—he whacked off a lock of his precious hair, which had never felt the edge of a knife. He was a good soldier, and seemed to be in accord with Jim, who anticipated no trouble with his co-chief. He would much rather, however, have ruled alone.

The death of Rotten Belly seemed to set off a chain of misfortunes for the Crows, and Jim was often hard-pressed for explanations of why his medicine was no longer powerful. For now the Crows were often defeated in their raids against their enemies; their villages were often attacked successfully; their horses were stolen and not recaptured. Food became scarce and the winter was exceptionally severe.

Jim felt that he knew the reasons for these setbacks, but they were reasons his companions could not understand. For one thing, because of their friendliness to the white men, the Crows had not acquired the supply of arms and ammunition and horses that hostile tribes had won through their attacks on trappers and traders. This gave their enemies a substantial advantage. For another thing, The American Fur Company had been pouring illicit liquor down the throats of the red men in the hope of winning their allegiance. Competing companies had retaliated by trying to outbid their rivals in this field. As a result, the Indians, even the Crows, had been sadly debauched.

There were other reasons far beyond the control of the victims of the changing times. Silk hats had replaced beaver in the great cities of the world, so that the trapping efforts of the Indians paid poorly. Now only the finest skins could be marketed at all, and these for far less in goods than formerly. Then, too, the Indians were realizing, too late, that they were being pushed from their ancestral lands and ways as white men in ever-increasing numbers infiltrated the Northwest. Now there were not merely a few friendly trappers. Now there were explorers, soldiers, missionaries and settlers who took the best lands for their own and held onto them by force of arms.

The Crow village seemed to receive the brunt of all these disasters. It was filled with despair. From morning till night the widows of slain braves screamed and howled. Blood was everywhere as fingers were lopped off in lamentation. Faces were continuously daubed with mourning paint. Jim began to grow weary of the howling and the blood and the misery all around him. The happy, carefree days were gone, and Jim felt the hopelessness of a leader who can do nothing to alleviate the anguish of his people.

One day Jim sat before his lodge, his chin dropped upon his chest, trying to decide on some plan of action that would bring happiness back to the miserable village. Blue Flower brought their son and set him on the blanket beside his father. Jim's eyes lighted at sight of the little fellow as he rolled and tumbled in the sunshine.

The sight brought back memories to the watching man: memories of himself as a child, first on the Virginia plantation and later at his father's place in Missouri. He saw himself fighting with Tom. He remembered walking with his father, being taught to shoot. And this thought brought a great wave of homesickness.

"Your father sits beside you doing nothing," he muttered to his small son, "but where is *my* father? When I left him he was old and ill, and I have let fighting and trapping and the business of this nation wipe his image from my mind. What am I doing here, anyway? Why do I listen to this howling? What would Tom think if he could see me now? I'll wager a prime beaver pelt that he would not deign to spit on me!"

Jim looked down at his buckskin shirt and leggings,

elaborately decorated now that he was head chief. Suddenly they looked wild and ugly and it was an effort to remember what each decoration signified.

Jim's unhappy meditation was interrupted by a commotion as a small band of newcomers rode into the village. He leaped to his feet and went toward the horsemen.

He was still a good distance away when he heard the trappers' yell, "Wah—hooo!" in a voice he could never forget. He ran to the horseman in the lead.

"Black Harris, you old coyote!" he cried. "What brings you here?"

Harris's shrewd dark eyes regarded Jim for a moment and then an ear-splitting yell brought several Indians running.

"Jim Beckwourth! Gar! Ye still hangin' around these here parts! I've heerd tell many a yarn about ye."

"Get down! Get down!" Jim urged. "You must stop awhile and rest—and eat——"

"Eat! Gar, I'll tell ye, Jim, I'm so hungry I could eat buffler hoofs, that I could. And my pardners here, too. We ain't had a mouthful of decent food fer two days now."

He dismounted and called to his companions to do likewise. Crow women stepped forward and took the horses aside.

"Come to my lodge, all of you. We'll have a meal ready in no time," Jim urged.

The trappers agreed joyously, and all made their way to Jim's main lodge. When they entered, they were astounded at the luxury of robes and blankets and weapons.

"Wagh!" Black spat a stream of tobacco juice, "ef this ain't a hangout, this child wouldn't know. Ye must be some punkins in this nation, eh?"

While Blue Flower and others prepared the best meal they could scrape together, Jim and Black exchanged accounts of what had happened to them since they had last met.

"I was just sitting here thinking of old times," Jim said at last, a little sadly. "I guess I was just sort of wishing I could see some of my old friends again." He sighed.

"Wal, that's easy fixed," Black said with energy. "Jest pack up an' come along with us. We're on our way now to Fort Cass. Take a little holiday, Jim, an' see what's goin' on in the world."

Jim's eyes lighted. "That's what I need, Black!" he agreed. "I'll do just that."

Black and his fellow trappers stayed the night in the village. When they rode out next morning, Jim was with them. And not only Jim, but Blue Flower and little Black Panther as well.

"I'm leaving Long Hair in charge here," he explained. "I want to get away from all the misery and unhappiness for a little while."

Jim's plan to escape did not work out. As soon as he was out of sight, Long Hair ordered the Crows to strike their village and follow their chief down to Fort Cass. When Jim awoke on his second morning at the fort, he was amazed to see the Crow village set up just outside the stockade. There was nothing for him to do but join them.

When Jim had been elevated to the rank of co-chief of the nation, he had been given his final name of Medicine Calf. Now his Dog Soldiers surrounded him and begged him to make one grand raid against the Blackfeet.

"Let us wipe away our sorrow. Let us avenge our slain heroes!" Pine Leaf urged. "We can leave the women and children here, safe near the fort. Our enemies will not be expecting us to leave the good times here to make an attack. Consider this, Medicine Calf! There will never be a better time!"

Jim hesitated. Even if the raid was successful, the loss of a single Crow brave would mean renewed mourning. And he was sick and tired of the howling and the blood and the painted faces.

"My medicine says it is not a good time," he demurred.

Pine Leaf's dark eyes looked upon him scornfully. "What has become of your powerful medicine?" she asked. "Why do you not propitiate the Great Spirit so that you will be strong again?"

"Yes!" the soldiers echoed. "We must make sacrifice to the Great Spirit so that Medicine Calf will again go to battle."

They selected their finest horses, painted a representation of the sun upon their sides and turned them loose on the prairie as an offering to the Great Spirit. And while they were waiting for this sacrifice to take effect, a band of Blackfeet raided the village one night, driving off many horses.

"It is a sign!" Pine Leaf said. "The Great Spirit wants you to avenge our loss."

Jim saw that he could delay no longer. Dressing for war, he set out with his Dog Soldiers. After several days they came upon a small band of Blackfeet with the stolen animals. Jim's warriors greatly outnumbered the enemy, and they easily retrieved their own animals and all of the Blackfeet horses without losing a man. The Crows were jubilant. It was their first entirely successful raid for many moons. They laughed at Jim for saying his medicine was no longer powerful.

The Crows did not hurry on their return trip. They had left the enemy afoot and were not afraid of being followed. But this time Jim misjudged his adversary, and the mistake caused him the worst defeat of his entire career.

The next day, while the Crows were moving leisurely across an open plain, they were attacked by a great body of Blackfeet, outnumbering the Crows four to one. Jim saw there was slight chance of escaping. He ordered some young boys to drive the horses to Fort Cass and wait there for two days. If the warriors did not come in by that time, the boys were to return to the Crow village and report that Jim's band had been rubbed out. Then Jim turned his attention to the desperate plight of his men.

A terrific battle followed. Jim's men would have been wiped out, but they found a sort of pit, or hollow, into which they leaped. From this refuge they made sorties against the foe. Thinking they had the Crows trapped, the Blackfeet sallied up to the mouth of the pit and rained arrows and bullets upon the crowded defenders. Sick at the thought of this inglorious end to his career and the tragic death of those who had trusted him, Jim fought with unusual recklessness.

At last an old warrior said, "Let us not stay in this hole to be shot like dogs. Let us go out and break through the ranks of the Blackfeet. They cannot kill us all. Some will get away. I will go first. I can break through their ranks alone."

There was no other hope, so with the old warrior leading the way, the Crows dashed out of the pit. Flailing their knives right and left, they literally hacked a way through the lines of the enemy.

Not all got through. Hunter, a white trapper who had been staying with the Crows, fell, mortally wounded. Little White Bear dropped dead across Hunter's body. Pine Leaf, fighting valiantly beside Jim, had a finger shot off. But a number did manage to hack their way through the enemy line and escape. Singing mournful dirges, their faces daubed with paint, they made their sorrowful way back to Fort Cass. Jim was miserable, for he knew that he was not proving to be the great chief Rotten Belly had expected him to be, and that the mourning and mutilating would be more gruesome than ever after this terrible defeat.

During these unhappy months, Jim had been sadly neglecting his work as agent for the American Fur Company. Now he was summoned to Fort Union to explain his neglect to Jacob Halsey, who was in charge of the company's affairs in that area.

"You know very well, Beckwourth," Halsey fumed, "that we have dealings with all the tribes in this region. When your Crows are out fighting, neither they nor their enemies can spend time trapping. Our business is falling off. It is your job to keep those Crows busy trapping——"

"That is impossible, sir," Jim pointed out. "The Crows are not the aggressors. When they are attacked by the other tribes, they have to defend themselves or be exterminated. Talk to the agents in the other posts—have them keep their Indians away from mine."

Halsey swore under his breath. Then he said angrily, "That is your old excuse, Beckwourth. But the fact remains that your Crows have got into more trouble since Rotten Belly died than they ever did before. But I am done with talking. You keep your Indians at home so that other tribes may have a chance to work a little, and the company may have a more profitable business! Or we shall have to engage another agent!"

Jim's nerves were raw from his recent setbacks. Halsey's words made him smart unbearably.

"You can do that, sir!" he retorted fiercely. "I am leaving the country!"

He had not meant to say that; he had not even made up his mind to go. But the words were spoken, and Jim felt a great wave of relief sweep over him. For that was what he must do. He must leave Absaroka and return to civilization.

As he rode back to the village his determination was assailed by doubts. How could he leave? He had been among the Crows now for nearly twelve years. It had been fourteen since he left St. Louis. What would he tell these people? How could he leave Blue Flower and his small son? How could he say farewell to Pine Leaf and his Dog Soldiers? But it must be done. He had come to the West seeking a fortune, but he had not found it. He had been taken a captive by the Crows, and, even though they thought they were doing him a favor by rescuing him from the white men, he had been a prisoner with no chance for escape. Now he would go.

On his last night before reaching the Crow village, he camped at an old fort near the river side, where some Crow hunters were staying. That night a band of Blackfeet came raiding. As Jim and his companions tried to drive them away, a bullet struck him, knocking him unconscious and from the saddle. Immediately a cry of dismay rang out. His companions rushed up. They carefully picked up Jim's unconscious form and carried him into the old fort to die. Samuel Tulloch, passing by in a boat on his way to St. Louis, saw the braves carry away Jim's inert figure. When he inquired what had happened, he was told that at last a bullet had killed Medicine Calf.

Word was sent to the Crow village and Jim's friends hurried to the fort. They brought his wives, his son, his horses and all his equipment to be with him at the end. But when the crowd of mourners arrived, howling and shrieking, they found that Jim was still alive. His medicine was still powerful. Apparently the bullet had hit his hunting knife and been deflected.

Jim seized upon this incident as an excuse to leave. He told himself that he would just go for a short visit to St. Louis and then return to the Crows. And he told the assembled nation:

"This is a sign! It is a message from the Great Spirit! I must take a trip down the river to St. Louis."

A cry of lamentation and negation rose. Jim held up his hand for silence.

"I shall not be gone many moons. While I am away, Long Hair and Yellow Belly will govern you. But let me counsel this: Do not send out any war parties while I am absent. Keep busy trapping and hunting. Take special care of all white men in your country. Have no fear. I shall return."

He picked up his son and held him close. This was the hardest parting of all. Jim's eyes were moist as he whispered, "You are the son of Medicine Calf. Never forget that. When I return I shall want to count the coups you have earned while I am gone."

He set the little fellow down and bade farewell to Blue Flower and Pine Leaf and the Dog Soldiers. Then Jim stepped into a boat loaded with peltries and ready to set out downstream. He looked back at the crowd waiting sadly on the bank. Then, as the boat swept out into midstream he turned forward. For the first time in many years he set his face toward his old home.

CHAPTER 12

Restless Days

On the way downstream, Jim took sick, and by the time the boat docked at St. Louis he was scarcely able to walk. In addition to his illness, Jim felt sadly let down when he saw that there was no one at the dock to greet the boat. He forgot that the fur boats were no longer exciting—that the people of St. Louis now had many other interests, and remembered only how the crowd had cheered and shouted when General Ashley's boat came in.

The boat carpenter offered to help Jim get to any place he chose, and Jim decided to try the house where, so many years ago, his older sister had lived. Perhaps she was still there, or the people could tell him where she had moved to.

On the way, Jim and the carpenter planned a practical joke. The carpenter rapped on the door, and Jim was delighted to see that it was opened by his younger sister, Louise. He did not step forward, however, but stood back out of sight, while the carpenter said gloomily that he was the bearer of sad news. Her brother Jim was dead.

Louise began to weep and said that they had had that news for some time. Mr. Tulloch had reported to the company that he had seen Jim's lifeless body carried into the old fort, and Mr. Chouteau had so informed them.

At this Jim stepped forward and said, "How d'ye do, Lou?"

Louise stared. Before her she saw a middle-aged man, dressed in deerskin shirt and leggings, ornamented with fringe and beads and porcupine quills, with ermine tails and long locks of hair that must be scalps. Long hair, black as an Indian's, hung to his hips; black eyes gleamed in the tanned and weather-beaten face. Only the voice and the phrase were familiar, and after staring a moment Louise cried, "It's Jim! It's my brother!" She threw herself into his arms.

After a moment she explained, "Mr. Tulloch thought you were dead!"

Jim grinned, "I thought so, too, for awhile there. But I'm very much alive as you see. And where's Matilda? Does she live here with you and my father?"

"Matilda is here. Your pa went back to Virginia five years ago—and died there." She turned and ran to the stairs calling, "Matilda! Matilda! Jim's come back!"

The carpenter chuckled. "Wal, now, Jim, yore taken care of. Guess I'll git about findin' my own folks. I'll see ye around town, though."

Jim thanked him for his help, but he was scarcely thinking of the man. He was remembering his father, how straight and soldierly he had been! How kind and affectionate to all of his children, and particularly to him! Emotional always and now sick as well, Jim felt tears gathering in his eyes. He was not given time to indulge his grief, for Matilda came flying down the stairs and into her brother's embrace.

"Jim! Jim!" she murmured, "I felt sure you'd come

back—I felt sure you couldn't die away out there, alone, so far from us all!"

Jim smiled at her fondly, recalling how Matilda had been the only mother he could remember. He was glad that he had come home to relieve their spirits of the anguish that the stories of his death had caused.

Now there was a great reunion and celebration. Jim's friends and relatives came crowding into Matilda's comfortable house to eat and talk and listen to his tales of Indian life. Under such love and care, he soon regained his usual good health, and went about the city looking for old landmarks and acquaintances.

St. Louis had changed in the years of Jim's absence. From a little town of less than five thousand people, it had developed into a thriving metropolis more than twice that size. Instead of the few fine houses owned by such aristocrats as the Chouteaus, with galleried porticos, wide lawns and esplaniered fruit trees, now there were many fine homes, surrounded by trees and gardens. The streets were paved with cobblestones; business houses boasted two stories and glass windows. Jim could not help marveling at the wealth of the city, and felt a surge of elation that much of this was due to the fur trade, in which he had had a helping hand.

Wandering around the city, visiting the theaters and taverns and shops, Jim ran into Tom Fitzpatrick. He was in a saloon at the time, and as soon as he saw his old friend he started forward impulsively to greet him. He stopped in his tracks as he heard Tom say scornfully, "There's the Crow!"

One of Tom's companions, a fellow named Forsyth, shouted, "Then I'm a Blackfoot, and I'll have his scalp!"

Jim didn't wait to see whether the two were in jest

or in earnest. Always quick to resent an insult, he leaped across the bar and began throwing beer glasses at Forsyth. As his arm swung back and forth, flinging his missiles with abandon, it was caught in an iron grip. The bartender twisted Jim's arm behind him, demanding that he stop at once, or be handed over to the constable. He gave up the battle and walked proudly and sullenly out of the saloon.

Later, Jim met William Sublette. He stared at his former captain, expecting an insult, even from this good friend. But Bill welcomed Jim earnestly, and seemed unaware of any of the disgraceful rumors concerning the trapper's behavior in the West. Encouraged by Bill's friendliness, Jim unburdened his grievance.

"I know tales have been told about me, but I want you to know that I never encouraged any of those Crow raids against white trappers. I did my best for both the trappers and the Crows, and many a time I shielded the trappers from injury. Why, when Tom Fitzpatrick and that Captain Stewart had that trouble, it was I, and I alone, who managed to get back the Captain's horse. But did he thank me? No, he called me a damned scoundrel!"

Bill nodded understandingly. "I know. I know. I'll see Tom and explain things."

He was as good as his word, and through his intervention the trouble with Fitzpatrick was smoothed over, and Jim and Tom became nominal friends again. But something was lost—some element had been dissolved by Tom's acceptance of those rumors.

There was one pleasant incident—Jim's visit to General Ashley's home. The general happened to be out when Jim arrived, but Mrs. Ashley greeted him cordially, invited him in to await her husband's return, and regaled him with cheerful anecdotes while he waited. He found his old employer's wife a beautiful and charming lady, well worthy of the great man she had married.

When General Ashley came home he was genuinely pleased to see Jim. The two sat for hours recounting adventures in the mountains, while Mrs. Ashley served refreshments and listened with interest.

But for Jim, St. Louis had lost its savor. He was restless and unhappy. He felt lost and alone and neglected. He had grown used to constant, strenuous activity, admiration and approval. He had grown accustomed to being one of the most important men in a community. Here he was nothing; no one seemed to know or care much about Jim Beckwourth. He grew homesick for the mountains and his Crow friends, and decided he would go to Pierre Chouteau, Jr., half-owner of the American Fur Company purchased from Astor, and try to get his old job as agent again. He could explain his trouble with Halsey and perhaps, being here where he could talk to the owners, he could obtain a better contract.

He had just reached this decision when a courier from the northwest came seeking him. There was trouble in the Crow nation. Some trappers had told the Crows that Jim had been killed by the Great White Chief. The Crows, under subchief Yellow Belly, had gone to Fort Cass determined to wipe out every white man there. According to their code, if a Crow was killed by white men, white men must be killed by Crows.

Sam Tulloch had managed to hold them off for awhile by promising that he would prove the stories of Jim's death were false.

"Now," the courier said, "you must return at once, Medicine Calf. Tulloch knew you were not dead, as he had believed when he came down to St. Louis, for we told him that you had recovered and gone downstream by boat. He urges you to return and save the fort."

Jim laid the situation before Pierre Chouteau, who suggested he return at once. "We'll fix the contract later," the owner declared. "There is no time to discuss it now. Hurry back and save our men." So Jim set out. At first he was exhilarated by the thought that he was escaping the humdrum life of the city. But the weather was bad; he was delayed by storms, swollen rivers, muddy roads. It took him fifty-three strenuous days to make the journey.

Jim was welcomed at the fort as the true savior of the garrisoned men. The gates were flung open to welcome him and as he rode through he cried, "Leave the gates open, now. There is no more danger!"

Jim was rather at a loss how to reprimand the Crows for their behavior. He knew they were acting upon long-established rules of conduct. Still, they must be made to understand that they could not kill white men at will, or over a fancied wrong. He finally decided on a way to handle the situation.

He went out to the Crow encampment near the fort and flung himself on the ground. There he sat, his chin upon his chest, a sullen frown upon his face. It was obvious that he was greatly displeased. The braves gathered and stood looking upon their angered chief. His wives formed a line and marched around him, each one pausing to lay a hand on the back of his neck in a gesture of humility and pacification. At last Yellow Belly spoke.

"What is wrong? What has angered Medicine Calf?"

Now Jim could state his grievance. "Didn't I tell you that I was leaving all the whites here at the fort in your charge? Didn't I tell you I would come back? Well, I return, and what do I find?"

Yellow Belly answered quietly, "Yes, you told me that, and I have done as you said. We have taken care of Tulloch and his men. We have brought buffalo for him to eat. Our women have carried wood and water for the people in the fort. Look, Medicine Calf! There is Tulloch inside the fort. There are his men. Are any dead?"

"No," Jim had to admit, "but you intended to kill them."

"Yes," Yellow Belly agreed, "if you had not returned before the cherries turned red, we would have killed them all. But it was only to avenge your death, of which the white man told us. Would you not do the same for one of us?"

Jim confessed that he would do the same for one of his Crow braves. But he still kept the sullen look on his face, to impress upon them the wrong they had contemplated.

So eager were the Crows to propitiate Jim and wipe that expression from his dark brow, that Pine Leaf decided to do the one thing Jim had wanted most. She offered to become his wife if he would stay among them.

"Warriors!" she said, "I am going to make a great sacrifice. I have trod the warpath with you. Now I will tread it no more!"

There was nothing for Jim to do but accept this generous offer. He shook off his melancholy, and became a happy Crow again. He rose from the ground, shook hands with his warriors, and began to tell of his adventures among white men.

The wedding feast was duly celebrated, and the normal life of the village was resumed. There were buffalo hunts, raids against the Blackfeet and Cheyennes, and other Indian activities. Jim took part in all this, but he was still discontented. He couldn't tell why. He didn't know where the trouble lay, but the old life had lost its glamor.

"Maybe I'm getting old," he thought sadly.

He wanted to get away, but it wasn't going to be easy. Jim began to recount to himself the things he should have done before leaving St. Louis. Chief of these was renewing his contract with Chouteau. If he did stay in this country, he should have that extra wage, that position of influence. He soon convinced himself that he should at least go down to Fort Union to renew his contract.

When the boats were ready to go downstream that fall, Jim was in one of them. He had told the Crows he would return in four seasons; they were not to believe any stories about his death; they were not to harass the white men. He had spoken in good faith, for when he told his new wife, Pine Leaf, and his young son good-by, he firmly intended to go only to Fort Union and then return. At Fort Union, however, he was unable to negotiate a contract. It was necessary for him to return to St. Louis to see Mr. Chouteau.

By the time he reached St. Louis, Jim didn't want a contract with the fur company. He sought out Bill Sublette and asked what he could do. Bill suggested that he join a company and go to Florida to help put down the Seminole trouble. Jim welcomed the suggestion, and nine days after his arrival in St. Louis, he was on a steamer bound for New Orleans with a company of mountain men, enlisted for the Florida war.

As soon as Jim reached the field of operations near Tampa Bay, he was engaged as a courier, and for the

next ten months he carried messages between the officers
of the United States outposts. Then the Seminoles sur-
rendered, and as ten months of Jim's year-long enlist-
ment had passed, he easily obtained a furlough for the
last two months and returned to St. Louis.

Back in the city, Jim found he was still not satisfied
with his former home. Now even Bill Sublette was gone.
He had left for the West to look after his fur trade—his
company was the last great rival of the American Fur
Company.

Bill's younger brother, Andrew, was looking for men.
He said to Jim, "Why don't you sign up with me? Louis
Vasquez—you remember him—and I have decided that
beaver is on the way out. From now on it'll be buffalo
robes that will sell. We're going to skim the cream off
that business—leave the beaver to Bill."

Jim shook his head. "I don't know, Andy. I found I
was fed up with the Indians——" he sighed. "But I've got
to do something, and I don't find anything in the city
that looks good to me."

"You'll find the southern lands and the southern Indians different from your Crows. Why don't you try
it, Jim? I need good men."

Jim's face flushed with pleasure at the hearty words.

"All right, Andy!" he agreed. "I guess I'm hooked for
another spell in Indian country. When do we start?"

CHAPTER 13

Jim Founds a City

XXXXXXXXXXXXXXXXXXXXXXXXXXXXXXXXXXXXXXXXXXXXXXXXXXXXXXX

Jim's eyes popped when he saw the caravan Andy's company had assembled. There were wagons packed with scarlet cloth, tobacco, blankets, beads, brass kettles, knives, mirrors, guns, ammunition—and kegs of whisky and rum. There were pack mules for the men, loaded with all the comforts of the trail. And there were fine saddle horses for the men to ride.

"You sure look prosperous enough, Andy!" Jim grinned.

Andy shook his head a bit mournfully. "None of this is paid for, and we owe every merchant in St. Louis. But if we can just bring in enough buffalo hides, we can wipe out our debts."

Protected by the guns of the crew, the caravan proceeded without difficulty to the headwaters of the Arkansas. They stopped for a night at Bent's Fort on the riverbank. Jim found some of his old companions there, for Taos, some 200 miles southwest of the post had become a favorite resort of mountain men, and Bent's was the most popular stopover on the way to and from the States. The Bents, of course, were rivals of the Sublettes in trading with the Indians, but the post was famous for the hospitality extended to all comers.

At Bent's Fort, Jim learned that the old gossip about his inciting the Crows to attack white men had percolated down into the desert lands. He was reminded of a thing he had almost forgotten among the Crows: that some white men could not forget his heritage; that in the eyes of these, any evil rumor could be true because his mother had been a slave.

It was Bent's head clerk, Lucas Murray, who brought the realization home to Jim. He began muttering in his tobacco-stained beard as soon as Jim came into the store. And when he was certain that Jim could not miss hearing him, he said to one of the loungers, "I can't see why Andy Sublette hired that danged rascal. No one but a low-down, half-breed, mulatto-Frenchman would massacre white men the way he has done."

It was the one insult Jim had never been able to stomach, and had got him into more than one fight as a boy. Hearing it again after all these years shocked him for a moment into inaction. Then he was reaching across the counter, dragging Murray out onto the floor. The frightened clerk began to yelp, but Jim flung him down and began to choke him. The men stood back, not interfering, but someone must have run to Andy Sublette with word of the ruckus. Andy rushed into the store and dragged Jim off the clerk, whose face was growing purple under the pressure of Jim's fingers.

Nothing came of the incident excepting that Murray and every one else was careful about the epithets they used in Jim's hearing. They recognized Jim's right to punish the clerk, for no mountain man worth his salt was expected to take an insult quietly.

Andy moved on a day's march from Bent's and then outlined his plan of action. He would return to St. Louis, leaving the work of obtaining the buffalo hides in the hands of his men, with Jim in charge. Jim's cheeks, sun-browned to a leathery toughness, flushed at hearing this. For the first time, after all his years of work, he was being placed in command of a brigade of traders.

Sublette went on, "No man understands the Indians better than Jim. And no man is less likely to be scared out by either Indians or rival companies. This is going to be a ruthless, cutthroat, get-what-you-can-as-you-can business and I am sure I have picked the right man to organize it. I'll start back tomorrow, and Jim can handle the work in any way he sees fit."

Jim had often contemplated what he would do if he were in the position of General Ashley or Tom Fitzpatrick or any other trader. His life among the Crows had shown him the mistakes these men sometimes made, mistakes he would avoid. The very first thing to do would be to establish a post for each tribe with daring, trust-worthy men in charge—men who would follow Jim's instructions to the letter.

As soon as Andy had left, Jim called the men together and outlined his plan.

"I aim to establish a post for each individual tribe—for the Cheyennes, the Arapaho, the Pawnees, and so on. Two men will be stationed at each post. I will travel from post to post leaving new supplies and collecting the buffalo hides and any pelts you have been able to obtain from the Indians. Sublette left a fine stock of goods with me—and—" he hesitated. He had tried to keep rum away from the Crows, but it had been of little use. Now, with all the traders relying on liquor as their chief bargaining agent, he would have to do the same or fail in obtaining hides for his employer. "And we have plenty of rum! However," he held up his hand as the men began to chuckle and talk, "I will instruct you how to handle this rum when you trade with the Indians. And I expect you to follow my instructions."

"Who do you aim to send to the Cheyennes?" Pierre Beauvais asked.

"I'm taking that post," Jim declared.

"Yore loony!" the men cried. "Ye've been a Crow—and ye know them Shy-anns hate the Crow's liver. They'll cut ye into little strips afore ye've taken ten steps into their village."

Jim shook his head. "I think I understand Indians. I know how to handle this."

Even William Bent, who came riding by and heard of Jim's reckless decision, tried to dissuade him. Bent wouldn't have minded getting rid of a determined rival, but he couldn't help expressing dismay at such a hare-brained project. Jim only shrugged. He was amazed that a man who had lived on the plains as long as Bent had done, a man with a Cheyenne wife, knew so little about how to handle a situation like this. Boldness was the key—boldness and rashness.

Jim established the easier posts, and left his men in charge. He supplied each with plenty of goods and enough rum to outbid any rivals. Then, with one companion and several well-laden pack horses, he set out for the village of Old Bark, a Cheyenne chief. When he reached the village he rode in boldly. The conical huts of bleached deerskin, painted with symbolic figures in the bold colors the Cheyennes loved, stood in a semi-circle facing a stream. Old Bark's lodge was the largest, and Jim rode up in front of it, dismounted and entered. His companion trailed at his heels, shivering in his moccasins. As soon as Jim entered, he knew he had been expected, for the lodge was filled with Cheyennes, whose fierce black eyes watched him closely.

Old Bark stared at the newcomer and through an interpreter he asked, "Who is this?"

Jim looked about him. He stood straight and arrogant and asked loudly, in Crow, "Is there a Crow here?"

At the word Crow every brave started. Dark hands dropped to knife hilts. One man stepped forward.

"I am a Crow."

Jim looked at him closely, but did not recognize the brave. However, his paint and his moccasins indicated that he was, indeed, a Crow, probably a captive who had been saved from death for some unknown reason.

Looking at Old Bark, but speaking to the Crow, Jim said clearly, "Tell the Cheyennes that I am a Crow chieftain. I have fought the Cheyennes for many winters. I have killed so many of their braves that I am buried in their scalps. I have taken their women and children prisoner. I have ridden their horses until their backs were sore. I have eaten their fat buffalo and their ripe cherries until I could eat no more. Now I have killed a great Crow chief, and I have had to run away or be killed."

From the corner of his eye, Jim saw his companion. The man had turned deathly pale and was trembling like an aspen in a wind storm. Inwardly Jim smiled, but his expression did not change. The poor fellow was certain they would both be scalped. He was wishing Jim had more sense than to brag about killing Cheyennes!

Jim went on, even more boastfully, "Tell the Cheyennes that I have come to them because I know they are the bravest Indians on the plains. If I am to die, I choose to have a Cheyenne kill me. I do not wish to be killed by cowards. The brave Cheyennes can kill me and cut me up into little bits and throw me to their

dogs. Then they can boast that they have killed a great
Crow chief—Medicine Calf!"

The interpreter had been following Jim, phrase by
phrase. When he came to the last words, to the name
Medicine Calf, Jim saw the fingers tighten on the knife
hilts. This was the crucial moment. If he had misjudged
his hearers, if Old Bark gave the command, Jim and
his companion would be torn to bits and their goods
confiscated. Jim never blinked an eye as he waited for
the result of his bold stroke.

Old Bark stood up and began to speak in Cheyenne,
which was translated into Crow by the interpreter.

"Warrior," the chief said, "we know you. We knew
you when you came in. We have known you in many
battles. Now we know you are a great brave. You say
you have killed many of our warriors. We know you
do not lie. We like a great brave. You shall live."

Jim could not control the flood of relief that swept
through him at these welcome words. He did manage,
however, not to let his exultation show.

"If you won't kill me," he said coolly, "I will live
among you. My strong arm will help you. But right now
I didn't come to fight. I came to trade with you. I've
brought many things you want and I will trade them
for the buffalo robes your wives and sisters have made
beautiful. But," he ended sternly, "I want you to understand that I will not endure any treachery. If one of
your braves lays a hand on me, I'll kill him."

Old Bark nodded. "It is agreed."

Now, the danger past, Jim could get down to business. He went outside and started to unpack his goods.
These he brought into the lodge and spread out on the
ground around the firepit. They made a fine showing

and the braves looked at the new goods eagerly for a moment. Then grumbles of discontent arose. Old Bark looked sharply at Jim and asked if he had not brought any rum.

Jim nodded. "I have much rum," he said quietly, "but I do not broach the kegs yet. Send in your squaws to trade. When they have finished, I will open the rum."

Old Bark grumbled, but Jim stood patiently waiting. This was one of the rules he had determined to follow, come what may. Jim had watched the traders and had decided that much of their trouble with the Indians came from their own stupidity and cupidity. The traders customarily opened the rum first, in order to attract the braves. The Indians would bring their own peltries and trade these for the firewater, which was usually diluted more and more as the Indians became less and less able to distinguish what they were getting. Often they would trade a prime beaver pelt for a mug of rum which was actually not much more than a mug of water tinged with the desired liquor. When the brave's own peltries were all traded, he would trade his horse, his arms, his wife's peltries and blankets—everything he could get his hands on.

The trader would think he had driven a sharp bargain, and he would count up his tremendous profits, chuckling, while the braves lay sleeping off the effects of the rum.

But another day came, when the brave awakened from his stupor. Then he found that he was poor. All his possessions were gone and he had nothing to show for them. His wives and children cried with hunger and cold. Then he knew he had been tricked and would go to the trader, seeking redress. The trader would swear he had given full value for every pelt, every horse and

gun and knife. The angry, frustrated Indian would answer with a bloody tomahawk.

Jim had often wondered why the traders did not see
that they were asking for death by this procedure. He
would do differently. He would let the squaws trade first
and after they had turned in their beautifully decorated
blankets for the objects they needed or wanted, he
would break out the rum for the braves. Then, when
the spree was over, though the brave might have nothing, his wives and children would be happy and he
could not accuse the trader of bilking him.

Old Bark grumbled for awhile, but Jim was firm, and
the trading had to go as he insisted.

Here in the Cheyenne village, Jim had many remind-
ers of his Crow friends. He knew their villages were
not too far away and that they would probably hear
that he was living among the Cheyennes, their enemies.
They would interpret this as a shrewd move on the part
of Medicine Calf to learn the secrets of the enemy. They
would believe that he would soon return to them. And
he wanted to return—to see Blue Flower and Pine Leaf
and, most of all, his son. But he knew that he could not
do this. If he returned it would mean he must stay—
he could not again get away. And he was not yet willing
to surrender his freedom and independence for the strenuous life of an Indian chief, with all the responsibilities
it entailed.

So for the next two years Jim stayed in the Southwest,
working among the Indians. When his year with Andy
Sublette was up, he took a job with Alex Warfield among
the Arapaho. Then he worked for William Bent at his
post on the Arkansas. There he became acquainted with
a trapper named Charley Towne, and the two decided
to throw in their lots together.

"I've heard a lot about Santa Fe and Taos," Jim told Charley. "Let's raise our traps and set out for the West!"

Charley chewed on the edge of his long mustache. "What would we do there, eh? See the senoritas? They're beauties, I've heard."

"I wouldn't mind seeing a pretty girl again!" Jim grinned. "But I've saved up some money. Maybe we could go into business out there."

Charley nodded. "They say the trappers outfit now at Santa Fe or Taos. We might find business pretty good."

The two packed up their scanty belongings and set out for the Spanish-American communities some 200 miles south and west of Bent's post.

Charley was right. Business was good and the senoritas were beautiful. Among these people Jim immediately felt at home. His flashing dark eyes, long black hair and swarthy skin were matters of no note here, and in the constantly moving stream of humanity passing through the town little attention was paid to what a man had done or to what rumor said he had done.

In the Spanish village of San Fernandez de Taos, just outside of the Indian pueblo, Jim and Charley built an adobe store, planning to stay for awhile. Jim was now forty-three years old, and he decided it was time to settle down. To help him carry out this resolve he married the handsome Senorita Louise Sanderville of Santa Fe, and became an active member of the settlement.

This didn't last long. By October of the following year, 1842, Jim had sold his store and was on the move again. He still intended to lead a quiet life, but this time he was going to try running a post of his own. He had already picked out the place, a lush spot where Fountain Creek entered the Arkansas River, one day's travel above Bent's Fort. Jim felt that this would make an excellent stopping place for the increasing numbers of caravans and travelers streaming westward.

When he and Louise arrived at the choice spot he found some of Bent's former employees camped there, and Jim enlisted their help in building his "Pueblo." They all went to work with a will, made sun-dried adobes for the walls; sharpened pickets for the stockade; and erected stout lookout towers. Inside the walls of the "fort" were numerous small rooms, where the workers settled down for the winter.

The land was rich, and Jim and Louise started a small truck garden. Jim knew that the one thing craved most greedily by travelers was green "garden sass" and he aimed to make his garden pay well.

As news of the new fort drifted about, trappers in the area wandered in and stayed. Some of these had Indian wives and families of half-breed children. As Jim watched these youngsters playing in the dust he couldn't help thinking of little Black Panther and wondering how he was and what he was like. He would be a young boy now, probably eager to go out on a raid. Jim remembered Rotten Belly's request, "Tell my wife to tell my sons who their father was. Do not let them forget!" He was sure that Blue Flower and Pine Leaf would never let Black Panther forget that he was the son of Medicine Calf. He would take a trip up into Absaroka someday and then what rejoicing there would be. But not now— not with this new post of his flourishing so lustily.

Some of the trappers, weary of the vagrant life, built somewhat better huts and cabins. They, too, turned to farming, and little patches of pumpkins, corn, wheat, potatoes and greens sprang up all around the "fort." Travelers stopped to rest and stayed for days—paying

Jim well—intrigued by his stories of his experiences among the Crows. His storytelling ability was in demand here as it had been around the campfires of Ashley's men.

Jim was prospering in a quiet way. Indians trusted him and brought in pelts and buffalo robes. There were caravans always coming or going. Life was sunny and good, and Jim let himself enjoy it. For the first time in years he assumed the trade-mark of the white trader—a grizzled beard. Among the Indians he had kept his face clean-shaven, as theirs were. Even when he was trading with Arapaho and Cheyenne he had maintained the smooth cheeks the red men admired. Now he let his beard grow. He assumed his place as head of a community.

CHAPTER 14

The Troubled West

×××

Peace and inaction were foreign to Jim's nature. A year had scarcely passed before he was itching for new adventures. Travelers who stopped at the pueblo were full of excitement about California. It was a land where there was perpetual spring; crops grew without the onerous burden of irrigation; roses bloomed all winter. As Jim listened, he became eager to take a look at this new land.

At the same time, conditions around Jim were growing troubled. There were rumors that the United States was going to war with her neighbor, Mexico. Mexicans in the region became insolent and suspicious. Often they refused to trade with Americans. Jim reasoned that it might be a wise move to try trading with the inhabitants of that fabulous land on the coast of the Pacific. He bought a supply of rum which he traded to the Indians for horses; packed up a large supply of goods, and with fifteen men set out, leaving Louise with her relatives in Santa Fe.

El Pueblo de los Angeles, Jim found, was not much different from Santa Fe or Taos. There was the same cluster of small huts, the same narrow, crooked streets, ankle-deep in dust in summer, knee-deep in mud in winter. But he found a number of old friends and acquaintances. Among these was John Rowland, who had brought a party of twenty-one out in 1841 and was now established as a solid citizen of El Pueblo. He told Jim, "This is virgin country, Jim. Great fortunes are going to be made here, and we're among the first!"

But Jim had been in California only a few months when the tide of trouble that had disturbed New Mexico was felt here. Jim coolly considered what his shrewdest move would be. He went to Rowland.

"It looks like we're in for some fighting," he said. "Not only Americans and Mexicans fighting each other, but Mexicans fighting Mexicans."

Rowland nodded. "Governor Micheltoreno has been a cruel and despotic man. True, he was appointed by President Santa Ana and is the legal ruler of California. But he maintains his office with the help of a crew of cutthroats and ex-convicts he brought with him."

"They're a bad lot, all right," Jim agreed. "They steal and murder. I've managed to keep out of their way so far, but it's risky."

"Well, the Mexicans are going to revolt, as sure as beavers have tails. And it won't be long now."

"Who's going to lead them?"

"General José Castro. He used to command the army. He's a good man."

"You going to side with Castro?" Jim asked casually.

Rowland nodded. Then, looking shrewdly at Jim, "Oh, some of the Americans will side with one man, some with the other. They'll calculate who is going to win and join him. I understand that Captain Sutter, up on the Sacramento, is on Micheltoreno's side. And some of the Englishmen will join one, some the other. But I'm for Castro. I figure he'll win. And everything I have is bound up here in El Pueblo. Common sense, as well as my own private sympathy, compels me to join Castro. What about you?"

"Well," Jim tugged at his beard thoughtfully, "I reckon you're right. If it comes to a fight, I'm with you."

It did come to a fight of sorts. Jim collected all the traders and mountain men that he knew and rode out to join Castro, who easily "took" Los Angeles, fort, arsenal and all.

For some weeks there was desultory fighting here and there, until Micheltoreno was driven out and a new governor, Don Pio Pico, was installed. Governor Pico chose Los Angeles as his official residence, and sent Castro north to Monterey with his troops. The two of them commanded, they thought, all of California.

The Americans in the north, however, had decided that this was a good time to seize California for the United States, and thus put an end to the troubles they had endured under the inefficient Mexican government. They were the more determined to do this because they knew that the British settlers were contemplating a similar coup on behalf of Great Britain; and they feared that the Russians at Fort Ross might have the same ideas.

Down at Los Angeles, Jim heard that Colonel John Charles Frémont, an American soldier and explorer, had captured Monterey and was leading a company southward to take Los Angeles. Now Jim was torn by a new dilemma. He had never yet met this Frémont, though he had heard many stories about him. At Bent's Fort he had learned that Kit Carson was often Frémont's guide, and had been all the way to the Northwest and the Pacific with the great explorer. Antoine Roubidoux knew the dashing officer and old Tom Fitzpatrick, himself, had been with Frémont on the trip to Oregon and

California. As Jim had listened to tales about the exploits of the adventurer, he had felt the sharp gnawing of envy. How had it happened that he had always been somewhere else when Frémont passed along the trails of the West?

Now Frémont was marching down California. He would probably be at Los Angeles soon. Jim was torn by a fierce desire to gather up his friends and ride north. He could easily imagine himself at the head of a compact, well-trained, well-armed little band, riding up and saluting. "Colonel Frémont! Here I am with my men at your service, sir!"

However Jim's shrewd mind saw the risk involved in such an act. If he rode north, his friends here would consider him a turncoat. He who, a month ago was fighting beside them, would now be on the opposite side. If the Americans lost, his life here would be miserable. Even if they won, his trade with the natives would be ruined.

Riding north was impossible. To the south lay Mexico, and Jim was not ready to cast his lot wholly with the Mexicans. At the west lay the Pacific. Jim decided the only way for him to travel was eastward.

Collecting a small company of five of his most trusted associates, he headed back for Santa Fe. As they traveled along he saw the herds of fine, fat horses that belonged to the Mexicans. They were more or less unattended, as their owners were busy fighting. Avarice sprang up in Jim.

"My country's at war with the Mexicans," he rationalized. "If I take these horses, I'll hamper the enemy. And if I turn them over—sell them," he amended rapidly, "to our troops, I'll be helping as much as if I'd fought beside Colonel Frémont."

He shouted an order to his men and they rode out to round up the animals. From then on it was a race—Jim's little troop driving off every Mexican-owned horse they could find. For the first five days they scarcely stopped to eat or sleep. Then, considering that they were fairly safe, they rode on at a more leisurely pace.

They arrived at Jim's old post on Fountain Creek to find it was still a bustling, though tiny, community. There they learned that American soldiers were marching to Santa Fe. Colonel Stephen Watts Kearny was not far away with his Army of the West. To Jim this was excellent news. He remembered the young officer who had met General Ashley at Henry's old fort and rode out to meet the troops with his band of fresh, fine horses. The Army of the West, having marched hundreds of miles in desert land without enough forage or water, had lost many animals and needed horses badly. Jim had no trouble getting a good price for his fine California mounts. He then offered his services to Kearny.

"You know this country well, I suppose?" the commander asked, fixing his cold blue eyes upon Jim.

"I do, sir. It's been my home for years."

"Well, then, come along with me to Santa Fe. When we get there, I will use you to ride express between that place and Fort Leavenworth."

Jim rode back to join the troops. On the way he reined up sharply, gave a halloo of delight.

"Hiya, Tom! You old grizzly! How come you're riding with Colonel Kearny? Last I heard of you, you were with Colonel Frémont—and he's in California, isn't he?"

Fitzpatrick grinned. "How are you, Jim? You're a sight to behold, out here in this forsaken desert. Yes, I started out with Colonel Frémont, but at Fort Leavenworth I was assigned to guide Lieutenant Abert's command—to catch up with Colonel Kearny and march on to Santa Fe."

"Guide it, Tom? Why, you've never been in this country before—"

Jim stopped suddenly. He had just remembered that Tom had been on the way to Santa Fe some fourteen years ago, when his companion and partner, Jed Smith, had been killed by Comanches.

Jim rode along beside Tom, asking eager questions about the white-haired guide's experiences in the past years, listening to tales of adventure, and adding some anecdotes of his own.

At last Tom said, "You've been in this country a long time, Jim. What do you think of our chances to take Santa Fe and the surrounding country?"

Jim answered readily, "There'll probably be some fighting—at least if Governor Armijo gets a force of fighting-mad Mexies together. And they could do damage if they take a stand in one of the mountain passes— Raton for instance. The Mexicans don't hanker to have the Americans take over. But on the other hand, they hate Armijo—and he's a coward. He'll probably turn tail and run. I don't think you'll have much real trouble. Colonel Kearny——"

"General Kearny, Jim. An express brought in his commission as Brigadier General this morning. The troops will be told tonight."

Tom relayed Jim's opinion to Kearny and the army advanced, cautious and ready for any emergency. They captured a few spies but they met no real resistance.

As they came to each small Mexican village along the road, General Kearny rode in, hoisted the Stars and Stripes to the top of a tall pole, and called the people together. Then he made a speech, telling them that they were no longer Mexican subjects, but now owed their allegiance to the United States.

"We come as friends, not enemies," the General said, his cold blue eyes staring frostily at the crowd of men, women and children. "I absolve you of all allegiance to the Mexican government and from all obedience to Governor Armijo. He is no longer your governor. I am your governor."

Mingling with the crowd, Jim heard the exclamations of surprise, saw the looks of incredulous wonder. How could this be? How could an American come here and, without a blow, change them from Mexicans to Americans? It was beyond comprehension, but, they shrugged, if it was so, it was so.

General Kearny promised that his troops would not harm or steal from peaceful citizens, but would protect them from the raids of Navaho and Apache. "But," he ended grimly, "Listen! He who promises to be quiet and is found in arms against me, I will hang!"

Village after village was thus taken without a shot being fired. But no one, from Jim to General Kearny, himself, expected Santa Fe to fall that easily. Runners came in daily telling of thousands of Mexicans, armed to the teeth, waiting in the dangerous Apache Pass, not far from Santa Fe. As they drew near the treacherous defile, two Pueblo Indians came dashing up, their arms and legs flailing the sides of their tiny burros.

They came up to Kearny, their faces radiant with joy and excitement. One of them shouted, "They are in the canyon, my brave! Pluck up your courage and push them out!"

The troops heard a command and advanced at the ready. But before they reached the Pass, a large, fat fellow came riding up on a tiny donkey so small that the man's legs nearly reached the ground. He rode directly to the general, extended a fat, dimpled hand, and said, "Señor, I am the Alcalde of Pecos. I come to tell you that Armijo and his troops have gone to hell and the canyon is all clear."

The alcalde was right. The Army of the West marched into Santa Fe, that ancient capital, without a challenge. The flag was hoisted, Kearny gave his speech, and New Mexico was safely in American hands.

Jim hastened to the Sanderville home to announce joyfully to Louise that he was back. Mrs. Sanderville opened the door, and when she saw Jim she gave a cry of alarm and dismay.

"Jeem! Jeem! It is you! You return now, too late! Too late!"

A tremor of apprehension ran through Jim. "Why?" he cried. "Has something happened to my wife?"

"Ah, Jeem! She is gone! Some Californios came here. They say you fight with General Castro against the Americanos. They say the cause is hopeless and that you would certainly either be killed or taken prisoner by the Americanos. So Louise," she shrugged and spread her hands in a gesture that spoke eloquently of the logic of Louise's decision, "Louise, she not want to be widow for long time. She marry Antonio Lucasto. They go to Sonora, to Senor Lucasto's mines."

Jim stared at the woman for a long moment. Then he shrugged. "Well," he said without anger, "I can't say that I blame her. I have been reported dead before, and the rumor was believed by those who loved me."

As he turned away to walk slowly up the dusty little street toward General Kearny's headquarters, he was thinking, not of Louise, but of Blue Flower, the mother of his son. She had wept for him for four days when she had thought him dead. And then she had gone on about her work in the Crow Village with no thought of leaving. Pine Leaf? If he returned to Absaroka now, would he find her waiting? Absaroka! Young Black Panther! They were things to dream about, and to return to someday.

True to his word, Kearny summoned Jim and put him into service carrying messages between Santa Fe and Fort Leavenworth. While Jim was thus occupied, Kearny hastily threw up an American post, which he named Fort Marcy. Then, leaving Colonel Sterling Price in charge of that area, the general marched on west. He had orders from Washington to take California and establish himself as commander of that region.

Riding express did not occupy all of Jim's time, so he invested his profit from the horse-selling in a small hotel in Santa Fe. Between his trips to Fort Leavenworth, one hundred thirteen miles away, Jim enjoyed running this establishment. There was always something happening—travelers stopping with news of war and adventure; fandangos and fiestas; drunken brawls and boisterous escapades.

The Mexicans, though they had accepted General Kearny's dictum, were not content. Resentment and hatred fermented into open hostilities. General Kearny had promised to protect the peaceful citizens from Indian raids, but his troops were ineffectual against the wily savages. A desperate storm was brewing, unsuspected by the Americans.

In the middle of a bitter cold January night, Jim was awakened by a loud knocking at his gate. When he threw it open, his old friend and partner, Charley

Towne, almost fell into his arms. The man was inco-
herent with cold and terror and weariness. Jim got him
inside and poured hot soup and coffee into him. When
the man was a little calmer, Jim said quietly, "Now tell
me, Charley!"

Towne told him. There had been an Indian uprising
at Taos. Many Americans had been killed.

"Governor Charles Bent—his whole family wiped out
as they lay asleep!" Towne muttered. "My wife's father
warned me as soon as he learned what was afoot, for
I think all the Mexicans and Indians in Taos knew what
was happening. My wife, you know, is a native, so her
father knew. He got me a good horse and I managed to
escape. I've ridden as fast as I could through the snow—
it's fearful in the mountains. I had to get here to warn
you—we don't know how widespread the revolt is going
to be."

"I must notify Colonel Price at once!" Jim said, pulling on boots.

Charley shook his head. "He's been told. An Indian
has taken word to him. They aren't all in the revolt."

"We'd better go, too," Jim insisted, "you can give a
much better account than any Indian."

Colonel Price lost no time in placing guards at stra-
tegic points in Santa Fe and assembling his troops to
march to Taos. He had only a small force. Some of the
soldiers had gone on with Kearny; others were with
Colonel Doniphan on the Rio Grande; still others had
marched southward with Colonel Clarke. Price summoned all the traders, trappers, clerks and merchants in
the town. It was a motley crew that he headed through
the blizzard-swept mountains toward Taos.

As the troops approached the pueblo, the revolutionists with their leader, Pablo Mantoya, who called himself the Santa Ana of the North, took refuge in the adobe church, where they were surrounded and, after a brief siege, were captured and hanged.

Jim was sent at once to Fort Leavenworth with news of the tragic event. While he was gone, the Apaches attacked a party of mountaineers among whom were several of Jim's friends. His old partner, Charley Towne, was killed in the skirmish. When Jim heard this news on his return to Santa Fe he shook his head sorrowfully.

"It doesn't seem to matter who it is—if a man lives long enough in the West the Indians will rub him out at last. I've been danged lucky, so far."

One day in the spring of that year, 1847, Jim met Kit Carson, on his way to Washington with dispatches from California.

"Californy's ourn, by heck! An' Colonel Frémont should hev the glory!" Kit declared. "But Gen'ral Kearny thinks he's the boss out thar an' gives orders right an' left!"

As Kit elaborated on his adventures with Colonel Frémont in the California War, Jim grew more and more envious. He felt that he should have obeyed his own wishes and gone north to join the daring officer whose exploits in the West had made him a hero to his admirers. Jim sighed. It was too late to think now of lost opportunities for adventure.

So he went on riding express for the army. Between trips he "collected" horses—by trade with the Indians, by rounding up loose animals on the prairie, by purchase. These animals he sold to the troops, always, it seemed, in need of fresh mounts. From time to time he was engaged as a guide to conduct emigrant trains on their way West. In this capacity he traveled every known trail westward, from the Gila River on the south to the Platte in the north and "Get Jim Beckwourth" came to be a common expression for all who needed a man who knew the West.

CHAPTER 15

And at the End — A Crow

The last dispatches handed to Jim at Leavenworth were addressed to California. He delivered these to the officers at Monterey, and then found himself at loose ends. His service with the army was finished and he was free to take any other employment.

The ocean and the coast had little appeal for Jim, so when the steamship *California* docked at Monterey on its way to San Francisco and on upriver to Sacramento, he went aboard. It would carry him toward the mountains, and when he left the ship he could make the rest of his way on foot, if necessary.

One bright morning Jim stood watching the pleasant landscape as the ship steamed slowly upstream. A fellow traveler came and leaned on the rail beside him.

"Goin' to the diggin's?" he asked by way of making conversation.

Jim shook his head, "I'd like to get hold of some of that gold," he admitted, "but I'm no man to dig it out of the ground."

"Where you bound fer, then?"

"I don't know. Any place inland. Absaroka——" He hadn't meant to say that last word; it came from his tongue without warning. But Absaroka was on his mind and he realized now that unconsciously he was heading toward the land of the Crows.

"Absaroka?" his companion repeated. "What's that?"

Jim, always ready to talk, launched into a description of the beauties of the northern region. His longing for the land and the people where he had spent such wild, free years was so evident in his voice that his companion asked, "So ye're going back, eh?"

Jim pondered that question. Then he said slowly, "I don't rightly know. Every time I finish a job I think now's the time to go back. But I never go. Guess I'm afraid."

"Think mebbe they'll scalp ye when ye git there, eh?"

Jim shook his head. It wasn't anything like that. It wasn't anything he could put into words, but it had to do with his return to other places he had left, and to his one return to the Crow country. Things always changed; they were never the same when you went back after an absence. It was best to look for something different, something new.

"Wal," his companion interrupted his thoughts, "I've been thinkin' there's money to be made *at* the mines, but not *in* them. Those fellers are so danged busy diggin' they won't stop to git in supplies. Ef I had a good pardner, I'd start carryin' food and clothes to them. Bet I'd git rich quicker'n some of them diggers."

Jim's eyes brightened. Sure! That was the thing! He was a trader. He knew what sold well to the Indians, and white men were not much different. He thrust out his hand.

"You've got a pardner, mister! I'm him."

They hunkered down on the deck and began making plans. At Stockton they left the boat, laid in a supply of goods, and started for the mines. Jim was in business again, and for a couple of years he attended to it. He built the first frame building—a small store—in the Mexican camp of Sonora some fifty miles east of Stockton. But a permanent home seemed to scare Jim. No sooner was the building up than he sold out his interest to his partner, and, with a horse and a pack set out to tramp the trails of the Mother Lode country.

This was the life he loved. He wandered where he pleased; hunted when he wished; stopped at the cabin of any mountaineer to tell yarns; lived with stray bands of Indians. And so, wandering over the mountain trails one day early in 1851, Jim made a discovery. He found a beautiful, grassy valley rimmed with mountain peaks, where, he was sure, no white man had ever set foot. On one side were the headwaters of the Yuba River, flowing west, and on the other the beginnings of the Truckee, flowing east. This lush valley was an easy pass between the snow-capped, granite peaks of the Sierras.

Jim was jubilant. This was his find. He could build a road here—up the eastern slope and down the western, and this road would pass through the new little town of Marysville. The community was striving to get established, while its rival to the south, Sacramento, was flourishing, largely because it was on an established emigrant road. Jim's shrewd mind grasped the possibilities. The landowners, merchants and hotelkeepers of Marysville would be glad to finance such a road. He could build a cabin here and reap the benefits of the stream of emigrants that would flow across his valley. He had given up his pueblo on Fountain Creek because of the Mexican trouble, but he was wiser now. He'd stay here and found a settlement that would carry his name down to posterity, as his father had done in Missouri.

It was a bright dream, but like so many of Jim's dreams, was doomed. He found the landowners of Marysville eager to have the new road built, but before they could do anything their entire city was burned to the ground.

Jim had the satisfaction of seeing his name in the paper. The Marysville *Herald* for June 3, 1851, proclaimed him "the discoverer and projector of this new and important route. Mr. Beckwourth states that he now has several men at work cutting a wagon road." It wasn't much, but he clipped the story and carried it with him to show to his friends.

Jim still had faith in his pass. He went up to the lovely valley in the spring of 1852 and built a sturdy house—the first to be erected in Sierra Valley. Soon emigrant trains were winding past his door, and his cabin grew into a substantial trading post.

In one emigrant train, late in 1854, there happened to be a newspaperman named T. D. Bonner. He had become ill on the road, and by the time he reached Jim's place, he was too sick to continue. He decided to stop here awhile to recuperate, but the winter snows came and he had to remain until spring. During the long evenings beside Jim's roaring fire, Bonner listened to the old mountaineer's tales of that early West when trappers and Indians ruled.

"Your life ought to be made into a book, Jim!" Bonner exclaimed more than once. "Why, man, no one knows the old days better than you do. And your life among the Crows! I'm going to write it!"

So, as Jim reminisced, Bonner took careful notes.

Often he would stop his pencil's racing across the page and look up. "How can you remember so much?" he would ask in wonder. "Even the number of General Ashley's horses. And that was nearly thirty years ago!"

By spring Bonner had enough material for a book—Jim's complete biography up to the year 1855, when he was 57.

When the book was placed on sale in San Francisco, it caused no little stir. Jim was so well known all through the California mountains that many wanted to read his story. There were those who roared with laughter and remembered that Jim had a reputation as a gaudy liar. They branded every incident as a fabrication. There were others, however, who were amazed at Jim's remarkable memory. For every incident of historical record took place largely as he had described it, with the official persons he named taking the parts he ascribed to them. And, while Jim was undoubtedly the hero of every event, as he told it, those who knew of the actual happenings shrugged. "That's probably the way it seemed to him," they said tolerantly. "It's only natural!"

Jim was delighted with the book. He carried it with him in his saddlebag whenever he traveled, and on the slightest provocation would produce it to astound his companions.

"Why, even General Ashley or Tom Fitzpatrick haven't had a whole book written about them!" he often exclaimed.

The book had an unforseen effect, however. The vigilance committees which had sprung up in many of the mining communities looked askance at Jim's tales of Indian fighting. The old stories of his inciting the Crows to attack white travelers were revived. Jim was requested to leave California. He packed up and sadly departed from the beautiful valley which had seemed like Eden to the aging wanderer. He left behind him his name for the first settlement in Sierra Valley, for an imposing butte that towered above it, and for the now important pass through the mountains.

In spite of his superstitious dislike of returning to places he had once loved, Jim made his way to his little pueblo on Fountain Creek. It was gone. The materials from the walls and stockade had been used by a group of St. Louis prospectors to construct cabins in a new little community they called Fountain City. This was actually only a small trading post to supply gold-hungry prospectors on their way to Cherry Creek where gold had been discovered in 1858.

Here Jim met his old trapping companion, Louis Vasquez, on his way northward with a caravan of supplies for the prospectors. He offered Jim a job, and the two went on together.

"Remember my old fort on the Platte?" Louis asked. "Well, that was very near where ze gold, it was discovered. Eh, bien! I did not know that gold was there." He shrugged. "But I think I get ze gold after all. for these goods which I will sell to those too busy prospectors."

"I did the same thing in Californy," Jim nodded. "It's a danged sight easier than digging."

Jim was eager to catch up on the news of the Plains, from which he had been absent some ten years.

"Whatever happened to Jim Bridger?" he asked.

"For long time, Jeem Breedger was my partner. We had a post at Fort Laramie. Then Jeem moved over onto ze Green River. You remember it, yes? He built a post there and I for awhile joined heem. We had a most good place and made pretty good money from ze emigrants who wished to get to Oregon. Then, about eleven years ago ze Mormons come to ze Fort Laramie. They do not like Jeem. They go on to ze edge of ze Great Salt Lake. Then they ask Jeem to leave his post. I do not know just what took place, but Jeem, he go until Colonel Johnston's army come out to fight ze Mormons last year. Then Jeem he hurry back to his post. The army wintered with heem last year, and paid well. Jeem, he is there now, I theenk."

"And Tom Fitzpatrick?"

Vasquez shook his head sadly. "He died in Washington, eet is four years past now. He was buried in ze, what you say, Congressional cemetery."

Jim spat. "Dang it! He'd rather be buried on a mountainside!"

They arrived at their destination to find it a rude little community of mud huts. There were really two communities, one on each side of the now-famous creek: St. Charles on the east and Auraria on the west bank. Louis chose the St. Charles side, built a frame store, and set his goods out on display.

The town boomed and the partners prospered. When business was slack in the store, Jim could always get a job piloting wagon trains. His fame as a guide and his reputation for getting along with the Indians put his services in great demand. And there were plenty of wagon trains going west: Mormons from the East and from Europe on their way to Salt Lake City; gold-seekers hurrying to California; home-seekers rushing to Oregon. So, though Jim was now in his sixties, he kept busy at the strenuous life he loved.

It was as a guide that Jim had his final experience in Indian fighting. He was employed by Colonel John M. Chivington to lead the United States troops southward to the region of the Arkansas. When Jim set out, he was unaware of the true nature of Chivington's expedition, but before long he discovered it. And it was with bitterness and disgust that he led the soldiers to Sand Creek. There Chivington and his troops surprised and wiped out a camp of friendly Cheyennes.

The attack was made at dawn on November 29, 1864. In the camp were six hundred and fifty Indians, four hundred and fifty of them women and children. Practically everyone was killed; many were mutilated in a shocking manner.

The affair ended Jim's interest in white men. Suddenly he wanted to go back to the Crows. He had heard long ago that his son, Black Panther, was a brave and honored chieftain. He hoped that Pine Leaf was still alive. He would return to Absaroka.

Jim bought a supply of the goods he knew his people would most enjoy. Packing these on two animals and mounted on a fine horse, he set out toward the northwest. As he rode along he couldn't help seeing the changes that had been made since he left this region. For one thing, beside him as he rode marched the tall straight poles that carried the telegraph wires—the singing wires, as the Indians called them. There had been nothing like this thirty years ago.

And there were soldiers. Every few miles Jim ran into a group of mounted bluecoats, their uniforms stained and dusty, their faces leather-brown. They might be scouting parties or expeditions sent out to punish marauding Indians. For now, Jim soon learned, the Indian tribes had largely given up fighting each other and were united in trying to repel the white invader and to hold onto their traditional lands.

At last, on the North Fork of the Shoshone River, Jim saw ahead of him a band of Indians, whose paint he recognized with a surge of joy.

"Crow!" he shouted. He kicked his horse in the flanks and rode up to them, lifting his hand in a friendly greeting.

The Crows drew rein and watched the stranger, their eyes wary.

"Don't you know me?" Jim asked in Crow. He found that the language came naturally to his tongue. "I am Medicine Calf, the Crow chieftain. I have returned to my people after many, many snows."

The warriors looked at each other. They had heard tales of Medicine Calf—of his valor, his powerful medicine against all enemies. Could this gray-haired old man be that hero?

Then one warrior, somewhat older than his companions, stepped forward and examined Jim closely from head to foot. Suddenly he reached out and grasped Jim's left eyelid. Pulling on it none too gently, he stretched the skin as far as it would go, while he stared at the exposed portion. When he saw the mole, about which he had often heard, he turned to his companions.

"It is Medicine Calf," he announced with finality.

The others now clamored around him noisily, shaking his hand, jabbering with excitement. He must ride with them to the village. The people would be delighted to welcome him again, after his long years of captivity among the white men. How had he escaped this time?

Jim let them chatter. It was good that they furnished

their own explanation of his long absence. But he wanted news of his son.

"I have a son," he said, "Black Panther. What of him?"

The warriors shook their heads. They knew no Black Panther. Then Jim remembered that a brave received a new name with each step toward chieftainship. He would have to wait to learn who and what his son now was.

Jim's return was far different from his first visit forty years before. Now there was no old woman to claim him as her son, no Big Bowl as chieftain, no pretty sisters and stalwart brothers to make a fuss over him. The braves led him to the lodge of the old chief, Crooked Nose, whom, after a few minutes, Jim recognized as one of his former Dog Soldiers. And Crooked Nose recognized Jim at the same moment. There followed reminiscing and talk.

Then Jim asked about his son, and learned that the boy had grown into a fine warrior, had become a sub-chief, but had been slain in a battle with the Blackfeet.

"And Pine Leaf, the Crow heroine?"

"Pine Leaf waited for her husband for many snows. Then she joined the Dog Soldiers again and rode to battle. She took many coups, but finally she fell in the same battle as your son."

"My other wives?"

"Only Blue Flower, the mother of your son, remains. She is here in the village."

"Bring her."

Blue Flower came into the lodge. She looked closely at Jim and then said quietly, "Medicine Calf has returned to his people."

Jim took up his life in the Crow village quietly and

without ceremony. As if he had never been away, he assumed the place of an elder warrior of vast experience, knowledge and skill, but with too many years upon his head to permit him to ride out against the enemy.

Jim felt some disappointment in his resumed Indian life. It was not as it had been years ago. There were none of the old mountain men he had known, the beaver was gone from the streams, only a few buffalo remained. The Indians did not ride out on glorious, exuberant raids against other tribes. When they fought it was in sneak attacks on white emigrants or settlers. Many of the old, boisterous celebrations were no longer observed, or were muted to a mere echo of what they had once been. His people, Jim thought sorrowfully, seemed cowed and spiritless, and remembering Sand Creek, he knew why.

Now, instead of the gay and daring beaver trappers, a new breed of men infested Absaroka. These were the wolfers, who made their living by poisoning and skinning the gray wolves of the mountains. In the old days, no trapper would have deigned to skin a wolf, but now the pelts were considered valuable in the cities. Jim heard with distaste of how the wolves were caught by eating the poisoned meat of dead buffalo set out as bait. The coyote, more cunning than his cousin, was not so easily betrayed. He would slink close, sniff at the polluted flesh, look with his yellow eyes at the dead wolves, and turn away. His hunger was unappeased, but he was alive.

And there were other strangers in the land: men prospecting for gold, men trying to establish farms in the new country, stores and trading posts and forts filled with bluecoats. Jim saw all these changes with bleak eyes and heavy heart. He had known that things would be changed in Absaroka. He had put off returning as long as he could. But it was here, among these people and in this land, that he wanted to end his days.

Jim had forgotten how early winter came here in the north and how chill the autumn winds could be. As they whistled down from the north, Jim became ill. Aches and pains caused by long rides, exposure to cold and wet, hunger and fatigue, wracked his old body. Instead of talking, he crouched close to the fire hole and listened to others talk, while his thoughts wandered to the hot sun beating down on the red sands of New Mexico or to his snug cabin in Sierra Valley with its wide stone fireplace and its roaring flames.

The pains grew worse. Even dog stew did not taste good and his stumps of teeth could scarcely chew pemmican. His eyes were weak and watery, and as he turned the pages of his beloved book he could no longer read the print. He bent his head low over the pages and thought, this is all I have to show for my years of danger and hard work. Will anyone read it after I am gone? Will anyone remember that James P. Beckwourth ever lived? He did not know that at that very time his little pueblo was recovering from the vandalism of irresponsible passers-by, and was a real community soon to boast a newspaper, which would on June 1, 1868 carry a notice of the death of his old friend, Kit Carson. Nor did he dream that a few decades later steel rails would mark a shining path up his old wagon road and across his lovely valley, and that thousands would speed along past the site of his abandoned cabin where a few score had traveled before.

Jim managed to weather the winter of 1866-67, but he was too weak to rejoice when spring came again. He lay huddled on a heap of buffalo robes beside the fire hole, watching Blue Flower as she moved about the lodge. And now he was glad that he had returned to Absaroka. Only here was someone to care for him—someone of his very own.

Blue Flower hovered over the fire, her back to Jim, stirring the dog soup. Into it she put some savory herbs and brought a wooden bowlful to her husband.

"Drink!" she commanded.

Jim took a few swallows and lay back. A few moments later he became violently sick. After the spell had passed he lay there exhausted. Through his rheumy eyes he watched Blue Flower. Had she poisoned that soup, he wondered. It was the custom, he knew, when a Crow woman wished to keep the spirit of her husband near. In spite of the question in his mind, a feeling of tenderness welled up in him for this bent, gray, wispy woman who had remained true to him through all his long years of wandering. She had taken him back without question and had nursed him all winter. If she wanted to keep his spirit near he could not stop her.

He lifted a shaking hand to fumble at the amulet he had worn ever since his early days among the Crows. It was the first bullet that had knocked him to the ground when it struck his knife hilt. It was the embodiment of his powerful "medicine." Perforated and laced on a buckskin thong, with a large turquoise bead on each side, the amulet had never lost its meaning for Jim. But as he fingered it now, it did no good. Its power, like Jim's, was gone.

Blue Flower was coming toward him with another bowl of the soup. Jim could not bear the thought of the agony that followed his first taste of the brew. He shook his head.

"Take me to the post!" he muttered. "Take me to the post!"

Blue Flower did not argue. Obediently she went outside and saddled her horse. Then she fastened a travois to the animal. With the help of some of the braves, she wrapped her husband in buffalo robes and placed him on the travois. Then, mounting the horse, she started slowly down the trail toward the nearest post.

The sun was warm on the buffalo robes. Jim opened his eyes and looked up at the blue spring sky, at the pines, fragrant and whispering. Nearby a stream was gurgling over its rocky bed. Jim thought of beaver, and his legs began to ache with the coldness of remembered streams he had waded to set his traps. If Blue Flower would only hurry——

The travois dragged slowly along. Looking back, Blue Flower perceived a curious stillness and stiffness about the form wrapped in the buffalo robes. Dismounting she went back and examined him. Jim was dead.

Mourning loudly, daubing her wrinkled face with paint she had brought along for this purpose, Blue Flower turned back to the village. There the braves came out to meet her and finding that the great hero, Medicine Calf, was dead, they too began to mourn. Soon the entire village was weeping and shrieking their sorrow.

Jim's body was wrapped in a scarlet blanket and placed on a platform high in the branches of a tree. It would remain there, safe from prowling animals, until the flesh had decayed away. Then the bones would be taken down and buried.

When news of Jim Beckwourth's death reached Jim Bridger at Fort Phil Kearny, not far from the Crow village, the old mountain man and companion of Jim's trapping days shrugged.

"Tell his squaw to stop her mournin'. Jim's died as he wanted to die, amongst the folks he felt most to home with. It's a heap better'n some folks has struck it. And if I guess right, his squaw made sartin that his spirit would never git away frum Absaroka!"

Bibliography

Alter, J. Cecil, *James Bridger*, Shepard Publishing Co., Salt Lake City, Utah, 1925.

Bonner, T. D. *James P. Beckwourth, Mountaineer.* T. Fisher Unwin, London, 1892.

Camp, Charles S. (Editor), *James Clyman, American Frontiersman*, California State Historical Society, San Francisco, 1928.

Chittenden, Hiram M., *History of the American Fur Trade in the Far West.* Harpers, New York, 1902.

Dale, Harrison Clifford, *The Ashley-Smith Explorations.* Arthur H. Clark Co., Glendale, Calif., 1941.

DeVoto, Bernard, *Across the Wide Missouri.* Houghton-Mifflin, Boston, 1947.

Emory, Lt. W. H., *Lieutenant Emory Reports.* University of New Mexico Press, Albuquerque, N.M., 1951.

Federal Writers' project, *California*, A Guide to the State, Hastings House, N.Y., 1939.

Colorado. Hastings House, N.Y., 1951.

New Mexico, Hastings House, N.Y., 1939.

Gardiner, Dorothy, *The Great Betrayal.* Doubleday, Garden City, N.Y., 1949.

185

Gregg, Josiah, *Commerce of the Prairies.* University of Oklahoma Press, 1954.

Gudde, Erwin G., *California Place Names.* University of California Press, Berkeley, Cal., 1949.

Hafen, LeRoy R. and Ghent, W. T., *Broken Hand,* The Life Story of Thomas Fitzpatrick. Old West Publishing Co., Denver, Colo., 1931.

Hayne, Coe, *Red Men on the Big Horn.* Judson Press, Philadelphia, 1929.

Hinkle, Geo. and Bliss, *Sierra-Nevada Lakes.* Bobbs-Merrill, Indianapolis, 1949.

Howbert, Irving, *Memories of Life in the Pike's Peak Region.* G. P. Putnam, N.Y., 1925.

Irving, Washington, *Adventures of Captain Bonneville.* Cooperative Publication Society, N.Y.

Jackson, Donald (editor), *Black Hawk.* Univ. of Illinois Press, Urbana, Ill., 1955.

Lavender, David, *Bent's Fort.* Doubleday, Garden City, N.Y., 1954.

Lowie, Robert H., *Crow Indians.* Farrar & Rinehart, N.Y., 1935.

Morgan, Dale L., *Jedediah Smith.* Bobbs-Merrill, Indianapolis, 1953.
The Great Salt Lake. Bobbs-Merrill, Indianapolis, 1947.

Twitchell, Ralph E., *Santa Fe.* Santa Fe Publishing Co., Santa Fe, N.M., 1925.

Vestal, Stanley, *Joe Meek.* Caxton Printers, Caldwell, Idaho, 1952.

Warner, J. J., *Reminiscences of Early California From 1831 to 1846,* Southern California Historical Society, Los Angeles, 1906.

Index

A

Abert, Lieutenant J. W., 161
Absaroka, 93, 100, 118, 123, 155, 169, 170, 176, 180, 182
Alexander, Alec, 90
American Fur Company, 116-118, 122, 123, 127, 133, 141, 145
Americans, 157, 158, 160, 162
Antelope, Chief. *See* Beckwourth, James
Apache Indians, 162, 167
Apache Pass, 163
Arapaho Indians, 106, 107, 109, 148, 153, 156
A-ra-poo-ash, Chief. *See* Rotten Belly, Chief
Arikara Indians, 109
Arkansas River, 45, 106, 146, 153, 154
Armijo, Governor Manuel, 162, 164
Army of the West, 161, 164
Ashley, General William H., 43-46; 51-63; 71, 72, 75, 76, 78, 80, 85-89; 103, 105, 116, 140, 148, 155, 161, 173
Ashley, Mrs. William H., 140
Assiniboine Indians, 105
Astor, John Jacob, 116, 141

Atkinson, General Henry, 73
Auraria, 175

B

Bannock Indians, 78, 79, 91, 92
Bar-chee-am-pa. *See* Pine Leaf
Bear River, 79
Bear Wolf, 103, 104, 106
Beauvais, Pierre, 149
Beckwourth, Major James, 9-12, 18, 21, 24, 25, 27, 33-42, 74, 128, 138
Beckwourth, James P., birth, 10; appearance, 11; mother, 11; learns to shoot, 20; learns to read, 22; disposition, 23; goes to school, 24; skills, 24; expelled from school, 25; appearance at 14, 25; apprenticed as blacksmith, 25-26; popularity, 27; fight with master, 29-31; goes to lead mines, 36; gaudy liar, 37; life at mines, 39-42; employed by Ashley, 44; trip to Pawnees, 46; express rider for Ashley, 52; hunter on trip West, 54-63; trapper, 64-68; at Rendezvous on Green River, 69-72; re-

turn to St. Louis, 74-76; encounters with Blackfeet, 77-82; represented as a Crow, 92; captured by Crows, 96; identified and welcomed, 98; marries Blue Flower, 100; named Antelope, 103; leads Crows, 103-105; named Enemy of Horses, 107; shield device, 109; appearance as Crow, 111; meets Pine Leaf, 115; joins American Fur Co., 118; son born, 120; trouble with Rocky Mountain Fur Co., 121-123; named Medicine Calf, 130; visit to St. Louis, 135; back to Crows, 142; married Pine Leaf, 143; in Seminole war, 144; joins Andy Sublette, 145; founds Pueblo, 155; appearance in middle age, 156; serves Gen. Kearny, 164; in Pueblo Indian War, 166; to California, 171; discovers Beckwourth Pass, 172; biography written, 173; returns to Absaroka, 177-78; death, 182.

Beckwourth, Louise, 11, 42, 75, 76, 138

Beckwourth, Ma'am, 11, 75

Beckwourth, Matilda, 11, 42, 75, 76, 138, 139

Beckwourth, Tom, 9, 11, 12, 21, 22, 25, 28, 34, 42, 74, 128

Beckwourth's Pass, 172

Beckwourth's Plantation, 22, 23, 128

Beckwourth's Settlement, 42

Bent, Charles, 166

Bent, William, 149, 153

Bent's Fort, 146, 147, 153, 154, 155, 159

Bible, 21, 65

Big Bowl, Chief, 98, 99, 102, 107, 178

Big Horn River, 72

Big House, 12, 21

Black Hawk, Chief, 38

Black Panther (Jim's brother-in-law), 106, 109, 112, 113, 114

Black Panther (Jim's son), 120, 130, 134, 135, 144, 153, 155, 165, 176, 178

Blackfoot Indians, 80, 82, 86, 89, 90, 101, 102, 109, 124, 125, 131, 132, 144

Blackfoot Territory, 89, 94

Bloody Arm. *See* Jim Beckwourth

Blue Flower, 100, 112, 113, 114, 128, 130, 134, 135, 153, 155, 164, 178, 180, 181, 182, 183

Bluecoats, 43, 76, 179

Bolliére, 83, 84

Bonneville, Captain Benjamin Louis Eulaie de, 119, 120

Bonner, T. D., 172, 173

Bridger, James, 69, 72, 79, 89, 94, 95, 114, 174, 182

British Settlers, 38

Broken Hand. *See* Tom Fitzpatrick

Buenaventura River, 80

Buffalo Surround, 56, 57

Bull boats, 62, 72, 79

C

Cache Valley, 85

Calhoun, 84

California, 157, 158, 159, 165, 169, 174, 175

California, SS, 169

California War, 159, 167

Campbell, Robert, 70, 81, 82, 84, 89, 91, 93

Canada, 68

Carson, Kit, 159, 167, 180

Casner, George, 25-33

Castenga, 68

Castro, General Jose, 158, 159, 164

Cherry Creek, 174

Cheyenne Indians, 92, 93, 97, 110, 113, 115, 144, 148, 149, 150, 151-156, 167

Chivington, Colonel John M., 176

Chouteau, Pierre, Jr., 138, 141, 142, 144

Chouteau Family, 27, 28, 35, 51, 139

Chouteau Trading Post, 51

Christmas, 60, 112
Clark, Colonel John D., 166
Clements, Constable, 30
Clyman, James, 57, 63-69, 79
Comanche Indians, 162
Continental Divide, 44
Council Bluffs, 52, 74
Crooked Nose, Chief, 178
Crow Indians, 65, 72, 73, 92, et passim
Cut Face. *See* William Sublette

D

Dog Soldiers, 115, 121, 130, 131, 134, 135, 178
Dog Soup, 79, 181
Doniphan, Alexander, 166
Ducks, teal, 59

E

El Pueblo de los Angeles. *See* Los Angeles
Elk, 59
Enemy-of-Horses. *See* Jim Beckwourth
Engagés, 54
England, 38
Englishmen, 158
Eroquey, 83

F

Fitzpatrick, Thomas, 52, 57, 58, 59, 62, 63, 78-85, 120, 121, 122, 139, 140, 148, 159, 161, 173, 175
Flathead Indians, 81, 82, 89
Florida, 144
Forsyth, 159
Fort Atkinson, 54, 72
Fort Cass, 118, 130, 132, 133, 141
Fort Clark, 13, 112
Fort Laramie, 174
Fort Leavenworth, 161, 165, 167
Fort Marcy, 165
Fort Phil Kearny, 182
Fort Ross, 159

Fort Union, 116, 122, 123, 133, 144
Fountain City, 174
Fountain Creek, 154, 165, 171, 174
Fox Indians, 35, 37, 38
Fraeb, Henry (Old Frapp), 67, 69
Fredricksburg, 10
Free Trappers, 78, 80
Frémont, Colonel John Charles, 159, 160, 161, 167
Front Street, 33
Furs, 28, 35, et passim

G

Games, 9, 10, 20
Gardner, Johnson, 70
Gaudy Liar. *See* Jim Beckwourth
Gervais, Baptiste, 81, 82, 83
Gila River, 168
"Ginger Tea," 14
Glass, Hugh, 65
Golden Arrow, 71, 81, 83
Great Britain, 159
Great Salt Lake, 70, 77, 79, 83
Great Spirit, 106, 124, 125, 131, 135
Green River, 61, 65, 71, 174
Greenwood, Caleb, 70, 78, 89, 92, 93, 98
Grizzly Bear, 73, 74, 107, 108

H

Halsey, Jacob, 133, 134, 141
Ham, William, 63
Harris, Moses, 46-50, 51, 55, 56, 70, 79, 80, 129, 130
Henry, Andrew, 45, 72
Henry's Fort, 72, 161
High Lance, 119
Horse Creek, 65
Hudson's Bay Co., 69, 70
Hunter, 133

I

Indians. *See* under specific tribe names

J

Jackson, David, 70, 86, 88
Jesuit Fathers, 24
Johnson, Colonel, 35, 36, 39, 40
Johnson, Darwin, 35, 37, 38
Johnston, Colonel Albert Sidney, 174

K

Kansas River, 45
Kearny, General Stephen Watts, 73, 161-165
Keelboat, 31
Kennedy Family, 16, 17, 18, 38
Keokuck, 38, 39
Kipp, James, 109, 112, 113, 114

L

LaBarge, Joe, 63, 66, 67, 68
LaJeunesse, Baptiste, 54, 58, 59, 62, 63, 69, 84, 89, 101
La Roche, 76
Lisa, Manuel, 27, 28, 35
Little White Bear, 133
Long Hair, Chief, 126, 130, 135
Long, General Stephen, 61
Long's Peak, 60
Los Angeles, 157-160
Lucasto, Antonio, 164
Lucius, 14

M

Mandan Indians, 118
Mantoya, Pablo, 167
Marysville, 171, 172
Marysville *Herald*, 172
McKenzie, Kenneth, 116, 117, 122
"Medicine," 110
Medicine Calf. See Jim Beckwourth
Mexicans, 158, 162, 165
Mexico, 157, 159, 160, 162
Micheltoreno, Manuel, 158, 159
Mines, 35, 36
Mississippi River, 10, 38, 44

Missouri, 10, 11, 44; River, 10, 27, 28, 40, 51, 72
Monterey, 159, 169
Mormons, 174, 175
Morning Star. See Jim Beckwourth
Mother Lode, 171
Mountain Men, 69
Murray, Lucas, 147

N

Nam-i-ne-dishee, 125
Navaho Indians, 162
New Mexico, 158, 164, 180
New Orleans, 52, 144
New Year, 60
Newell, Doc, 70

O

Ogden River, 78
Ogden's Hole, 78
Old Bark, Chief, 149, 150-153
Old Betsy, 14, 15, 16
Old Gabe. See Jim Bridger
Old Glory, 70
O-mo-q-ua, Chief, 85
Oregon, 159, 174, 175

P

Pacific Ocean, 79, 157, 159, 160
Pawnee Indians, 45, 47, 49, 56, 57, 148
Pecos, Alcalde of, 164
Pellow, 76
Pico, Don Pio, 159
Pilcher, Joshua, 73
Pine Leaf, 115, 130, 131, 133, 134, 135, 143, 144, 153, 155, 165, 176, 178
Platte River, 44, 52, 168, 174
Portage de Sioux, 10, 38
Portuleuse, 80
Potawatami Indians, 39
Potts, Dan, 55, 56, 63, 79
Powder River, 93

Price, Colonel Sterling, 165, 166
Provost, Etienne, 70, 81, 82
Pueblo, 155
Pueblo Indian uprising, 163

R

Raton Pass, 162
Red Elk, 101
Republican River, 45, 49
Rendezvous, 62, 67, 68-72, 81
Revolution, American, 10
Richmond, 21, 22
Rio Grande River, 166
Rocky Mountains, 61
Rocky Mountain Fur Co., 116, 120, 122
Rotten Belly, Chief, 119, 121, 124, 126, 127, 133, 155
Roubidoux, Antoine, 159
Rowland, John, 158
Russians, 159

S

Sacramento, 158, 169, 171
Sage River, 80
St. Charles, Colorado, 175
St. Charles, Missouri, 42, 74
St. Louis, Missouri, 23, 24, 27, 28, 37, 40, 41, 42, 44, 45, 51, 52, 68, 72, 74, 78, 80, 86, 88, 92, 103, 134, 135, 139, 141, 145
Salt Lake Band, 69
Sand Creek Massacre, 176, 179
Sanderville, Louise, 154, 157, 164
Sanderville, Mrs., 164
San Fernandex de Taos, 154
San Francisco, 169, 173
Santa Ana, President, 158
Santa Fe, 68, 69, 70, 154, 157, 160, 163, 164
Sauk Indians, 35, 37, 39
School, 24
"Sea Faring Brigade," 15
Seminole War, 144, 145
Shabona, 39, 40

Shield Device, 109
Shining Mountains, 53, 60
Shoshone River, 177
Sierra Mountains, 171
Sierra Valley, 172, 173, 180
Simon, 21, 22
Sioux Indians, 109
Skin Trappers, 80
Smith, Jedediah S., 65, 68, 72, 78, 80, 85, 86, 88, 162
Snake Indians, 79-85, 91
Sonora, 171
Stars and Stripes, 38
Stewart, Captain William Drummond, 121, 122, 140
Stockton, 170, 171
"Stonies," 61
Stony Point, 10, 20
Sublette, Andrew, 145, 146
Sublette, William, 57, 58, 62, 71, 76, 78, 80, 85, 86, 88, 89, 113, 114, 140, 144, 145, 147, 138, 153
Sutter, John Augustus, 158
Sutton, John, 25

T

Tampa Bay, 144
Taos, 146, 154, 157, 166
Tewinty Mountains, 63
Tongue River, 120
Towne, Charley, 153, 154, 166, 167
Truckee River, 171
Tulloch, Samuel, 118, 123, 134, 138, 141, 143
Two Axe, Chief, 56, 58

U

Union Jack, 70
United States, 157, 159
Utah Lake, 80

V

Vasquez, Louis, 79, 145, 174
Vigilantes, 173
Virginia, 10, 11, 22, 128

W

Warpath Secret, 104
Warfield, Alex, 153
Washington, General George, 13
Washington, D.C., 75, 165, 167
Waterloo, 122
Weber River, 78, 80
Wellington, Duke of, 122
Whiskey, 112, 122, 152
White-Handled Knife. *See* Jim Beckwourth

William and Mary College, 22
Willow Valley, 77, 79, 85
Wind River Mountains, 93
Winter Camp, 78
Wives, Indian, 111, 142
Wolfers, 179

Y

Yellow Belly, 135, 141, 142, 143
Yellowstone River, 44, 72, 116, 118
Yuba River, 171